THE BRITISH ISLES

BY T. PICKLES, B.Sc.

FOR SENIOR FORMS

	s.	d.
THE WORLD	10	0
EUROPE	7	6
THE BRITISH ISLES	5	6
THE SOUTHERN CONTINENTS		
BOOK I. SOUTH & CENTRAL AMERICA	4	9
BOOK II. AFRICA	5	0
BOOK III. AUSTRALIA, NEW ZEALAND, & PACIFIC ISLANDS . .	4	9
A REVISION COURSE IN GEOGRAPHY .	4	9
MAP READING	4	0
INTERMEDIATE MAP READING .	5	0
NORTH AMERICA	5	9
ASIA AND EUROPEAN RUSSIA .	5	3
PHYSICAL GEOGRAPHY . . .	5	3
THE WEALTH OF THE WORLD: An Economic Geography . . .	9	6

FOR JUNIOR AND LOWER MIDDLE FORMS

MODERN SCHOOL GEOGRAPHIES

	s.	d.
AFRICA, AUSTRALIA, & NEW ZEALAND	5	6
NORTH AND SOUTH AMERICA .	5	3
EUROPE AND ASIA	5	9
BRITAIN AND THE MODERN WORLD .	5	6
GREAT BRITAIN AND IRELAND .	3	9
ELEMENTARY MAP READING .	2	8

PRICES SUBJECT TO ALTERATION

THE POOL OF LONDON

THE
BRITISH ISLES

BY

THOMAS PICKLES, B.Sc.

ILLUSTRATED WITH
83 MAPS AND DIAGRAMS
AND 8 PAGES OF
PHOTOGRAPHS

NEW EDITION

J. M. DENT AND SONS LTD.
BEDFORD ST. LONDON W.C.2

© Revisions, J. M. Dent & Sons Ltd, 1958
All rights reserved
Made in Great Britain
at the
Aldine Press · Letchworth · Herts
for
J. M. DENT & SONS LTD
Aldine House · Bedford Street · London
First published 1935
Last reprinted 1960

PREFACE

THIS book is intended primarily for pupils preparing for the 'Ordinary' papers of the General Certificate of Education. The course is that followed by the author in his own school, and is the outcome of a long experience in preparing several forms each year for these examinations.

The teacher of such forms has a twofold responsibility— that of training the minds of the most intelligent of our future citizens at a critical period in their lives, and that of preparing them for an external examination on the results of which their future careers often depend. This book represents the attempt of the writer to harmonize these pressing responsibilities in his own work, and it is issued in the hope that it will meet the needs of the large body of teachers in public schools and secondary schools who are engaged in similar work.

The subject-matter is that body of fact which now meets with general acceptance among teachers, examiners, and administrators as the basis on which the school course in the geography of the British Isles should be built. In the presentation of these facts the author has endeavoured to establish, by frequent illustration and numerous concrete examples, the causal relationships between natural advantages or disadvantages on the one hand and economic activities on the other. Within the limits imposed by such practical considerations as the number of school periods available, the age of the pupils, and the demands of the examinations, the attempt has been made to provide a survey of the geography of the British Isles which will not only be a workmanlike aid to preparation for the examinations in question, but will also form the basis for an intelligent appreciation of our social and economic problems.

Thanks are due to the following examining bodies for permission to reproduce from their School Certificate and Matriculation papers the numerous questions which are appended to chapters:

London University: Matriculation (L. M.); General School Examination (L. G. S.). Cambridge University: School Certificate (C. S. C.); Cambridge Local (C. L.). Oxford University: School Certificate (O. S. C.); Oxford Senior Local (O. S.). Northern Universities: School Certificate and Matriculation (N. U.). Durham University: Matriculation (D. M.); School Certificate (D. S. C.). University of Wales: Matriculation (W. M.); School Certificate (W. S. C.).

The weather charts in this book are based on Crown copyright material and included by permission of the Controller of Her Majesty's Stationery Office.

T. PICKLES.

Barnsley.

CONTENTS

PLATES

MAPS AND CHARTS

CHAPTER I

POSITION AND PHYSICAL FEATURES

The Position of the British Isles

The greatness and prosperity of Britain are due in no small measure to her advantageous position. If we turn the globe into the position in which the maximum amount of land is

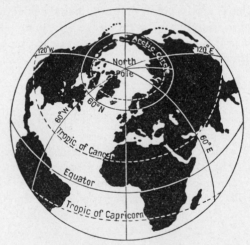

FIG. I. THE LAND HEMISPHERE

visible at a glance we shall see that Britain is almost in the centre of this land hemisphere (see Fig. 1). She is, moreover, situated athwart the great ocean highways leading to western Europe, where are crowded together most of the highly developed countries of the world, and where a very large

I

proportion of the world's manufacturing is carried on. Our country is, therefore, at the natural focus of the ocean trade routes, and has almost unequalled opportunities for world trade.

The proximity of Britain to the Continent has meant that in the past she has received several waves of immigrant peoples, who have intermingled to form a vigorous nation capable of developing the natural resources of the land, while the separation from the Continent has given freedom from invasion within modern times, thus allowing the peaceful development of industry and commerce.

From the climatic point of view, Britain is fortunate in having the variability of weather necessary for the main-tenance of health and vigour, without great extremes of heat or cold, rain or drought.

THE CONTINENTAL SHELF

Fig. 2 shows that our islands are separated from the Con-tinent by comparatively shallow seas which cover a broad submarine plain. This submerged plain is known as the *continental shelf*, and the edge of it, which coincides with the submarine contour of 100 fathoms (600 feet), is called the *continental edge*. The latter is the true edge of the Continent, and north-western Europe owes its present indented coast to the fact that after the Great Ice Age the level of the sea rose some 600 feet, submerging the great plain which formerly joined Britain to the mainland, and converting the lower courses of the rivers into many-branched estuaries.

This geological accident has had far-reaching effects on the history and development of our country. These effects may be summarized as follows:

(1) Our 'drowned' coast provides many good harbours,

which have greatly assisted the growth of commerce, and helped to make the British a seafaring nation.

(2) The tides rise to a greater height because of the existence of the continental shelf. In the open ocean the rise and fall of the tide is very small, but as the wave of the tide reaches

FIG. 2. THE CONTINENTAL SHELF

the shallow seas over the continental shelf it increases in height, thus penetrating far up the estuaries of the rivers, and allowing vessels to take their cargoes well inland.

(3) Quite apart from the above-mentioned increase in the height of the tide, the gradual slope of the continental shelf causes the tides to flow farther inland than they would if the coast coincided with the continental edge. This will be readily understood from Figs. 3B and 3C. In each case there is the same rise of the tide, but in Fig. 3C, where the slope of the sea-bed is less, the vessel is carried farther inland.

(4) The shallow seas over the continental shelf form excellent breeding- and feeding-grounds for fish. The food of fishes consists of microscopic plants and animals which are most abundant in water so shallow that sunlight can

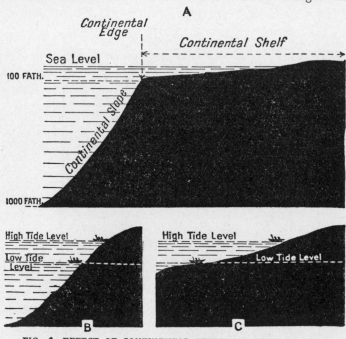

FIG. 3. EFFECT OF CONTINENTAL SHELF ON TIDAL WATERS
(Diagrammatic sections)

penetrate it; consequently the fish are most abundant on the continental shelf, where their food is most plentiful. Moreover, the seas of the continental shelf are so shallow that the bottom can easily be reached by trawls. The fishing industry of the British Isles is of great importance in itself, but the indirect effect of the industry as a training school for merchant seamen and for the navy has probably been of even greater value in the commercial development of the country.

How Nature Built Britain

Geologists who study the rocks know that several times in the history of the earth great mountain ranges have been heaved up by the forces of Nature, and have then been worn down almost to sea-level. Great Britain owes its present form to the fact that it is situated at the point where several of these mighty ranges of the past intersect.

The Highlands of Scotland are the most ancient of the British mountains. They are remnants of a great range which once extended from Scandinavia, far out into the Atlantic, possibly connecting up with the mountains of the eastern side of North America. During the hundreds of millions of years which have elapsed since these mountains were formed they have been worn down almost to sea-level, again uplifted, broken into huge blocks, and remodelled by frost and rain and running water, so that the Highlands as we see them to-day are merely dissected fragments of the pre-existing range. Scotland owes its form to five great faults, or lines of weakness along which portions of the crust have subsided (see Fig. 4). The Central Valley is a rift valley, formed by the land slipping down between the two parallel faults which run respectively from Helensburgh on the Firth of Clyde to Stonehaven on the east coast, and from Girvan to Dunbar (see Fig. 5). The Grampian Highlands are separated from the Northern Highlands by the great fault of Glenmore, and the Minch, which separates the Outer Hebrides from the mainland, is a submerged rift valley. It is interesting to note that the above-mentioned faults are continued through Northern Ireland, and converge near Galway Bay.   The structural features of Ireland are thus seen to

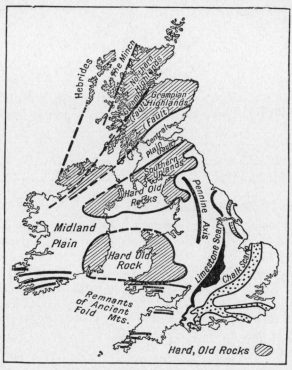

FIG. 4. BRITISH ISLES—STRUCTURE

be a continuation of those of Scotland, and there is no doubt that, in remote ages, they were parts of the same land mass.

The same north-east to south-west grain of the land is seen in the mountains of Wales and of south-eastern Ireland, and as these mountains are formed of the same kind of rock there is no doubt that they, too, were formerly connected.

The remnants of another vanished range, possibly only about half as ancient as the Highlands of Scotland, are to be seen in south-western Ireland, South Wales, and Cornwall and Devon, where the grain of the land runs from west to

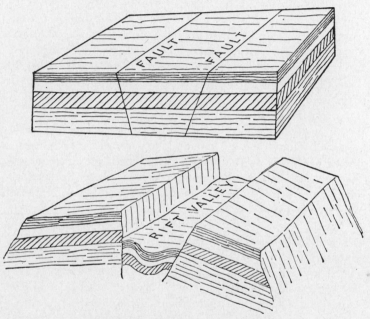

FIG. 5. FORMATION OF RIFT VALLEY

east. The ancient range, to which the name Hercynian is sometimes given, extended from south-western Ireland through central France into central Europe.

A third direction of folding is shown by the Pennines, which run from north to south. It is to the intersection of this line of folding with the north-east to south-west grain of the Caledonian ranges and with the west-to-east grain of the Hercynian remnants, that England and Wales, and the British Isles as a whole, owe their triangular outline.

HARD AND SOFT ROCKS

Rocks such as granite, limestone, and some kinds of sandstone, are said to be 'hard' because they are not easily worn away by the weather, while rocks such as shale and clay, which are easily worn away, are said to be 'soft.' The old rocks are nearly all hard rocks, because they have been repeatedly folded and compressed by the mountain-building process, and because any softer portions have long ago been worn away by the weather. Consequently the old rocks generally stand out as mountains, while the newer, softer rocks are worn down to form plains and low hills. Fig. 4 shows that all the mountainous districts of the British Isles are formed of hard old rock, while the lowlands are formed of newer, softer rocks.

On the English Plain the land is hardly anywhere above a thousand feet in height, but there are several prominent ridges running from west to east and from south-west to north-east. These ridges, which are called *escarpments*, are characterized by a steep slope on one side and a more gradual slope on the other side. They owe their origin to the fact that the land is composed of slightly tilted layers of alternately hard and soft rocks. Figs. 6A and 6B show the gradual development of such escarpments by the more rapid wearing away of the softer rocks. The more gradual slope is called the *dip slope*, since it follows, and is determined by, the dip of the layer of hard rock, while the steep slope is called the *scarp slope*. On a contour map the dip slope can easily be distinguished because the contours are farther apart and wind about more than on the scarp slope.

Will F. Taylor

HELVELLYN

Topical Press

KILLARNEY

The escarpments of south-eastern England fall into two groups, composed respectively of limestone and of chalk. The limestone scarps run from Portland Bill to the mouth of the Tees, and include the Cotswold Hills, the Northampton Uplands, the Lincolnshire Heights, the North York Moors,

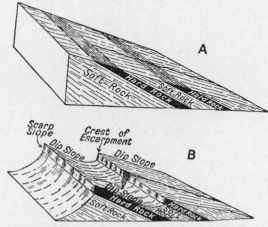

FIG. 6. DEVELOPMENT OF ESCARPMENTS

and the Cleveland Hills. The chief type of rock in this belt is a kind of limestone which is composed of tiny rounded grains like the roe, or eggs, of fishes, and which is therefore called oolite, or 'egg stone.'

The chalk scarps radiate from Salisbury Plain, and are due to the folding of a thick layer of chalk and other rocks. The Chiltern Hills run north-eastward and are continued by the East Anglian Heights, the Lincoln Wolds, and the York Wolds; the North and South Downs are inward-facing scarps which enclose the upfold of the Weald; and the 'backbone' of the Isle of Wight is formed by another upfold of the bed of chalk.

The Features of the Sea Coast

As has already been pointed out (page 2), the deep indentations of our coast are due to the submergence of the land and the drowning of the continental shelf. There is, however, a marked contrast between the western and eastern coasts, the former being much more indented than the latter. This contrast is certainly not due to the fact that the west coast is open to the full force of the Atlantic gales, while the east coast is apparently somewhat sheltered, for many of the inlets of the west coast are so winding and landlocked that storms hardly ever penetrate to their upper ends. The ruggedness of the west coast is due to the fact that the numerous belts of specially hard rock have withstood both the waves and the weather, while the somewhat softer rocks between were worn down to form valleys which were 'drowned' by the sinking of the land, thus forming the inlets between the headlands. In south-eastern England, where the hills are comparatively low, the coast is much less indented, though even here the ridges run out to sea as prominent headlands. Good examples of such prominent headlands which are the obvious counterparts of the ranges of hills, are South Foreland, which marks the end of the North Downs, and Beachy Head, which is the seaward terminus of the South Downs. There are, however, other projections on the coast which are simply low accumulations of sand and mud deposited by the currents and the tides. Examples of these are Spurn Head at the mouth of the Humber, and Dungeness on the south coast.

The Coal-fields of Britain

If the coal-fields are drawn on an outline map of Britain, they seem to be most irregularly distributed. If, however, they are drawn on a map showing also the old rocks and the high land, it immediately becomes apparent that they are situated on the dividing line between the old and the new rocks, and at the junction of the high and low land. (See Fig. 7.)

The northern and midland coal-fields of England are disposed symmetrically around the Pennine and Lake District highlands, and may be linked together by a great U passing round these highlands. The Northumberland and Durham coal-field on the east of the Pennine axis is matched by the Cumberland or Whitehaven coal-field on the western edge of the Lake District uplift, and the Yorks, Derby, and Notts coal-field on the east is balanced by the north Staffordshire and the south Lancashire coal-fields on the west. The reason for this symmetrical arrangement will be seen by reference to Fig. 26, where it is shown that the southern Pennines are like an arch from which the top has been worn away. Formerly the coal-measures, i.e. the rocks which contain coal-seams, were continuous over the whole arch, but the long-continued action of the weather has worn away the coal-measures as well as part of the millstone grit from the summit of the arch. Between the coal-measures of Yorkshire and those of Durham there is a similar, though much less pronounced fold, and it is probable that at one time the coalfields of northern England were all joined together.

The Midland coal-fields — those of south Staffordshire, Warwickshire, and Leicestershire — seem on the ordinary physical map to be exceptions to the rule that the coal-fields are situated on the edge of the high land and on the edge of the old rock. Detailed maps show, however, that they are all situated on the borders of 'islands' of ancient rock which rise up fairly steeply from the plain, and radiate fan-wise from the southern end of the Pennines.

The coal-fields of the Welsh border and of South Wales can

be linked by a line running round the edge of the Cambrian Mountains, and the Scottish coal-fields all lie within the rift valley, where they have been preserved from denudation.

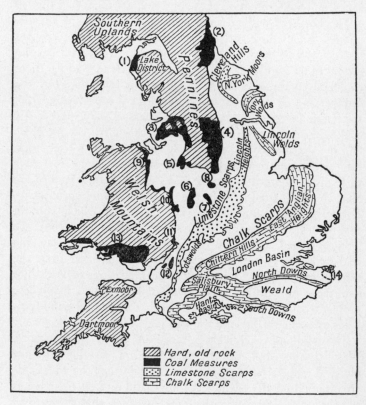

FIG. 7. ENGLAND AND WALES—COAL-FIELDS

(1) Cumberland or Whitehaven; (2) Northumberland and Durham; (3) South Lancashire; (4) Yorks, Derby, and Notts.; (5) North Stafford-shire; (6) South Staffordshire; (7) Warwickshire; (8) Leicestershire; (9) Flint and Denbigh; (10) Welsh Borders; (11) Forest of Dean; (12) Bristol; (13) South Wales; (14) Kent (concealed).

Fig. 7A shows the 'Divisions' of the National Coal Board, with their production as percentages of the total.

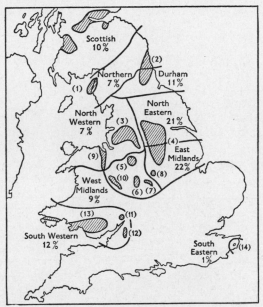

FIG. 7A. COAL-FIELDS: N.C.B. 'DIVISIONS'

Iron Mining

Nearly all the iron ore mined in Britain is obtained from the oolitic limestone escarpment which runs from the mouth of the Tees to Portland Bill (see page 9 and Fig. 7). The chief iron-mining areas are: (1) around Corby, Kettering, and Wellingborough in Northamptonshire; (2) around Scunthorpe in Lincolnshire; (3) in the Cleveland Hills of north-east Yorkshire.

The only important iron-mining area outside the limestone scarp is the Furness district of north Lancashire.

CHAPTER II

CLIMATE, FARMING, AND FISHING

CLIMATE

THE outstanding features of the climate of Britain are its humidity, its mildness, and its variability. These characteristics are due in no small measure to the fact that our prevailing winds blow from the south-west. As these winds blow from the ocean, they are mild in winter and cool in

FIG. 8. RELIEF RAIN AND RAIN-SHADOW

summer, and are heavily charged with moisture at all times. As they approach the mountainous areas near our west coasts they are compelled to rise, with a consequent lowering of temperature which causes condensation of moisture in the form of rain (see Fig. 8). The wettest parts of Britain are, therefore, those areas where high mountains lie near the west coast, and it is worthy of note that all such areas of heavy rainfall—the Western Highlands of Scotland, the Lake District, and North Wales—may be reached by south-westerly winds direct from the Atlantic. The eastern side of Britain is said

to be in the *rain-shadow*, since the winds have been robbed
of most of their moisture in their passage over the highlands
of the west.   Thus Valentia Island, which is situated off the
south-west corner of Ireland, has a total annual rainfall of

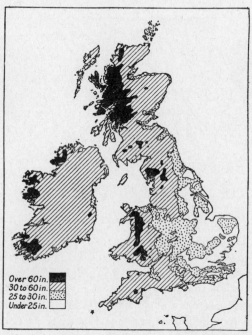

FIG. 9. ANNUAL RAINFALL—BRITISH ISLES

56 inches, while London has only 25 inches.   Stye, in Cumberland, has the highest recorded annual rainfall in Britain, 247
inches having been recorded, and Margate holds the lowest
record with 9·3 inches in 1921.

Though all parts of the British Isles are liable to receive
rain at any time of the year, autumn and winter are the

wettest seasons except in the district between the Humber and the Thames, where, contrary to the general impression, most rain falls in the summer half of the year. Oxford, for example, has 29 per cent of its rain in summer, and only 22 per cent in winter.

FIG. IO. THE GULF OF WINTER WARMTH
January isotherms: 32° F., 0° F.

So far as temperature is concerned, Britain is fortunate in having warmer winters than any other district in the same latitude. This 'Gulf of Winter Warmth,' which is well shown on the map by the northward bend of the 32° F. isotherm, is due in large measure to the prevalence of mild south-westerly winds. Another important factor is the Gulf Stream, which, flowing from the Gulf of Mexico, transfers a great deal of heat from equatorial regions to north-western Europe. This current would, however, have little ameliorating effect on our climate if the prevailing winds blew from the continent towards the ocean.

Another remarkable feature of our winter climate is that temperatures diminish not from south to north, but from west to east, the general trend of the isotherms being from north to south (see Fig. 11). As shown by the 40° F. isotherm, the north-west corner of Scotland is as warm in January as the coast of Sussex, and the lowest sea-level temperatures in the country are to be found in eastern England and eastern

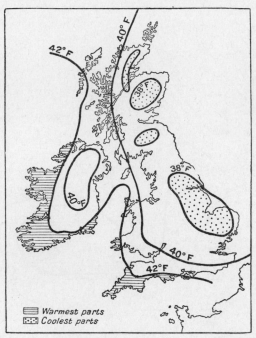

FIG. 11. JANUARY ISOTHERMS (SEA-LEVEL TEMPERATURES)

Scotland. The reason for these apparent anomalies of temperature is that the sun has little power in winter, so that the dominant climatic influence is the mild westerly wind which naturally brings more heat to the western than to the eastern side of the country.

In summer the dominant climatic influence is the sun, and

B 8·15–50 m

in that season the temperatures diminish from south to north, and the isotherms run roughly from west to east. Over the land, however, they make marked northward bends, indicating that the land is much warmer than the sea.

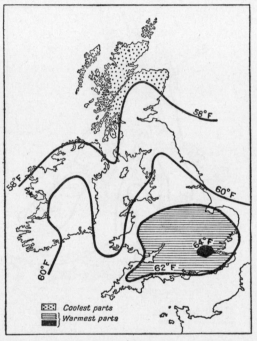

FIG. 12. JULY ISOTHERMS (SEA-LEVEL TEMPERATURES)

The 40° F. isotherm for January and the 60° F. isotherm for July divide the British Isles into four climatic provinces, of which the south-west is the most equable and the warmest in winter, while the south-east is the most extreme and the hottest in summer.

Though the westerly winds and the Gulf Stream are

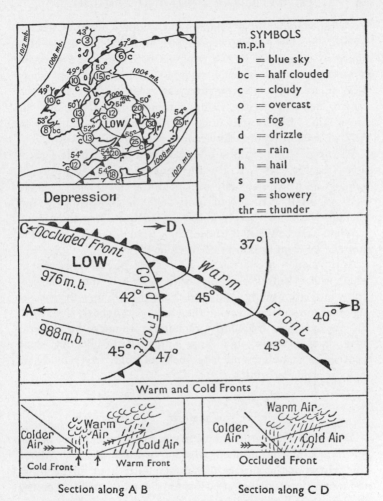

SYMBOLS
m.p.h

b   = blue sky
bc = half clouded
c   = cloudy
o   = overcast
f   = fog
d   = drizzle
r   = rain
h   = hail
s   = snow
p   = showery
thr = thunder

Depression

Warm and Cold Fronts

Section along A B

Section along C D

FIG. 13. DEPRESSION; COLD AND WARM FRONTS

important factors in our climate, our weather owes its characteristic variability to the depressions, anticyclones, etc., which
figure so frequently in the weather forecasts. A depression
is an area of low atmospheric pressure in which the winds
blow in an anti-clockwise direction round and towards the
centre, near which the rising currents of warm, moist air
cause rain. Depressions usually travel over our islands from
west to east, bringing heavy rain to each district in turn.

Warm and cold 'fronts' are associated chiefly with depressions (see Fig. 13). At a warm front warm, moist air is advancing and rising steadily over cold air, thus causing rather
heavy rainfall. At a cold front cold air is advancing and
pushing warm air sharply upwards, causing sharp showers.

When the body of warm air has been lifted clear of the
ground the front is said to be 'occluded.'

Anticyclones are areas of high atmospheric pressure in
which the circulation of the air is outward and clockwise.
The winds are usually light, and there is little upward thrust-
ing of one air-current over another, and consequently little rain.
As anticyclones frequently remain stationary for several
days, or even weeks, they cause long spells of hot, dry, clear
weather in summer, and long spells of cold, dry, cloudy or
foggy weather in winter.

FARMING

As most of the British people live in towns, we are apt to for-
get that farming is one of our most important industries. About
nine-tenths of the surface of our islands is used for farming,
about one-twentieth of our people are directly dependent on the
land for their livelihood, and the produce sold off farms represents about one-fifteenth of the total value of goods produced
in the country. The total number of people occupied in

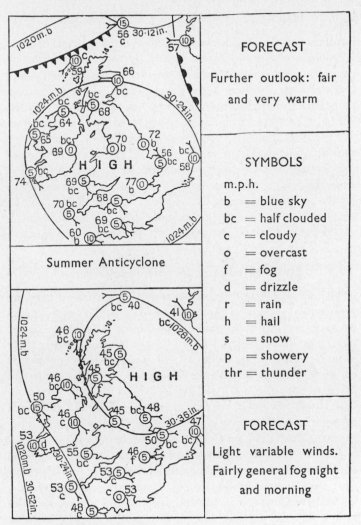

FORECAST

Further outlook: fair and very warm

SYMBOLS

m.p.h.

b = blue sky
bc = half clouded
c = cloudy
o = overcast
f = fog
d = drizzle
r = rain
h = hail
s = snow
p = showery
thr = thunder

FORECAST

Light variable winds. Fairly general fog night and morning

Summer Anticyclone

Winter Anticyclone

FIG. 14. SUMMER AND WINTER ANTICYCLONES

farming in the British Isles is greater than in such great farming countries as Canada, Australia, and South Africa; in proportion to her size Britain is one of the foremost sheep- and cattle-rearing countries in the world; and, again in proportion to her size, she produces three times as much wheat as the United States, four times as much as Argentina, and ten times as much as Canada. Above all, Great Britain is noted for the intensive character of the farming, the yield of produce per acre of farm land being much greater than in most other countries. The yield of wheat per acre, for example, is nearly 20 cwt., while in Canada it is only about 9 cwt., in Argentina 8 cwt., and in Australia only 5 cwt. Even so, we produce at home only about half our total food supplies.

TYPES OF FARMING IN THE BRITISH ISLES

Though there are large areas in the British Isles where the farmers are concerned principally with a single product such as wool, beef, or milk, the bulk of the farming is of a mixed character. This is especially true in the lowlands, where there is much arable land, for such land is always cropped on the rotation system. The details of rotation vary from district to district, but all are derived from the old Norfolk system in which wheat is grown the first year, root crops such as turnips or potatoes the second year, barley the third year, and clover or beans the fourth year. The chief advantage of this system is that, as different crops extract different types of plant food from the soil, the fertility of the land is maintained without the need for large quantities of manure. Moreover, the leguminous crops, such as peas, beans, and clover, actually add nitrate to the soil, leaving it richer in that constituent than it was before, and so preparing it for the wheat which is usually sown the following year. Of course, the farmer does

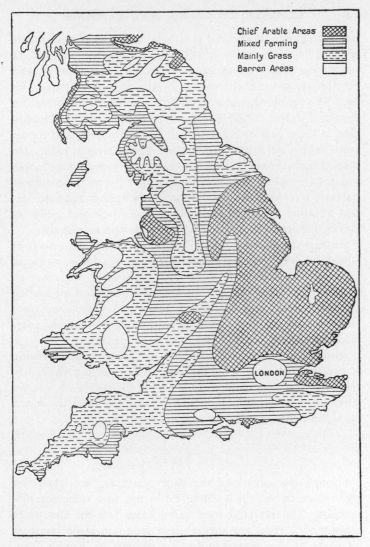

Chief Arable Areas
Mixed Farming
Mainly Grass
Barren Areas

LONDON

FIG. 15. LAND UTILIZATION

not sow all his arable land with one crop, but divides it into at least four parts, each of which is at a different stage of the rotation system.   Every year, therefore, he produces at least four crops, and in many cases, by substituting on part of his land peas for beans, and vegetables, potatoes, or sugar-beet for turnips, he often produces seven or eight main crops.   In addition, a large part of his land will be under grass and fodder crops, which will eventually be marketed as meat or milk.   On a good farm three types of grassland will generally be found, viz. meadow-land, which yields the hay harvest; permanent pasture, on which the animals graze in spring and summer; and rotation grassland, on which special grasses, such as clover, are grown in rotation with cereals and root crops.

Among the above-mentioned farm products some, such as wheat, barley, potatoes, and sugar-beet, are 'money' crops, i.e. they are sold directly as a source of income.   Others, such as oats, clover, and mangolds, are used on the farm for feeding the farm stock, and are thus transformed into horse-power for the work of the farm, or into such marketable commodities as meat, wool, hides, and dairy produce.

Although, as has been emphasized above, British farming is predominantly of a mixed and even complex character, there is a considerable degree of specialization in various parts of the country, since some parts are specially suited for sheep-rearing, others for cattle, and so on.

SHEEP-REARING

Sheep require dry land and short grass, and will thrive on poor pastures on which cattle could not find sufficient sustenance.   On wet land they suffer from foot-rot and other diseases, but they are nevertheless found in large numbers on some of the wettest hilly districts of the British Isles,

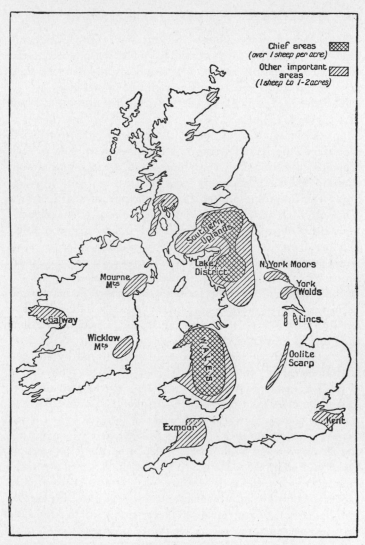

FIG. 16. SHEEP

though they may be almost absent from neighbouring low-lands which receive far less rainfall. The reason is that the sheep are quite tolerant of wet weather, provided the land is well drained, as it naturally is on the steep hill-sides.

The chief sheep lands of the British Isles may be divided into three groups, viz.:

(1) The mountainous districts, such as the Cambrian Mountains, the Lake District, the Pennines, and the Southern Uplands of Scotland, where the soil is too thin for arable farming and the pastures too poor for cattle.

(2) The limestone and chalk escarpments of south-eastern England, such as the North and South Downs, the Chilterns, and the Cotswolds. Limestone and chalk are composed chiefly of calcium carbonate, which allows water to soak through, leaving the surface dry, even after a heavy shower. Moreover, as the calcium carbonate is completely dissolved, instead of being broken up by the weather into grains of sand as in the case of other rocks, limestone and chalk hills have usually only a very thin covering of soil which is sufficient only for the growth of short, wiry grass. On such hills, there-fore, are found the two chief conditions required by sheep— a dry foot-run and short grass.

(3) The rather hilly arable districts, such as Lincolnshire, where the chalk and limestone escarpments are covered with a layer of glacial soil which enables arable farming to be carried on even on the hill-tops. Here, as well as in many other arable districts of Britain, the sheep are reared as part of the system of mixed farming. The system of rotation ensures that each year some of the arable land produces crops such as clover and turnips on which sheep can be fed; and the farmer is thus enabled to keep far more sheep per acre than is possible on the poor pastures of the western mountains, or even on the sheep-runs of the Downs. The sheep, moreover, improve

the land by treading and manuring it, thus preparing the field for the following crop of wheat. It is for this reason that the farmers often refer to the 'golden hoof' of the sheep. Sheeprearing has, nevertheless, greatly declined in recent years with the increased intensity of food production on the arable farms, especially on the limestone and chalk scarps.

CATTLE-REARING

In contrast to sheep, cattle thrive best on rather damp lowlands where the grass is long and rich. They are, therefore, most numerous on the clayey lowlands on the wetter western side of the British Isles, though even in the comparatively dry plains of the east large numbers of cattle are kept as part of the system of mixed farming mentioned on page 22.

Three types of specialization in the cattle industry may be noted, viz.: the rearing of young stock, the production of beef, and dairying. Stock-raising is carried on chiefly in the less fertile, rather hilly districts, which favour the growth of hardy animals for sale to the farmers on the neighbouring lowlands for dairy purposes or for fattening as beef cattle. Examples of such stock-raising areas are the Craven district of Yorkshire (in the upper valley of the Aire), the plain of Hereford, and the Buchan Plateau (the north-eastern shoulder of Scotland). The latter area is the home of the famous Aberdeen Angus and Shorthorn breeds, large numbers of which have been exported to Argentina to form the basis of the great meat-producing herds of that country.

Beef cattle are specially numerous on the moist, fertile lowlands where there are few great cities or industrial areas. Thus, the midland plain of Ireland, the lowlands of Cornwall and Devon, the Severn lowlands, and the north-eastern lowlands of Scotland are predominantly beef-producing areas.

Appox. 300 per 1000 ac.
" 200 " 1000 ac.

FIG. 17. CATTLE

The distribution of dairy-farming is determined very largely by accessibility to good markets in the form of large towns. This is especially true in the case of fresh milk which must be delivered daily, though modern methods of transport by road as well as by rail have enormously increased the areas from which the towns can draw their daily supplies. London, for example, gets much of its milk from Somerset, Newcastle is a market for the milk producers of the Solway plain, and Liverpool is supplied partly by the lowlands on the southern side of the Lake District mountains.

Dairy-farming areas which are remote from large centres of population must use their milk for the production of butter or cheese. Thus the Golden Vein of south-west Ireland, around Limerick, and the lowlands of Cornwall and Devon, are among the chief butter-producing areas in the British Isles. Specialization in cheese-making seems to be determined largely by local tradition and skill, and the varieties of the product are named after the areas where they were originally manufactured, e.g. Cheshire, Wensleydale (Yorkshire), Stilton (Huntingdonshire), and Cheddar (Somerset).

WHEAT

The conditions necessary for the successful cultivation of wheat are:

(1) A rather dry climate, with less than thirty inches of rain per year.

(2) Cool, moist weather in the early period of growth.

(3) Warm, dry, sunny weather for ripening and harvesting.

(4) Level or slightly undulating land to facilitate farming operations.

(5) Fairly heavy clayey soil which provides abundant plant food, and holds up the heavy head of wheat.

(6) Easy transport to a good market.

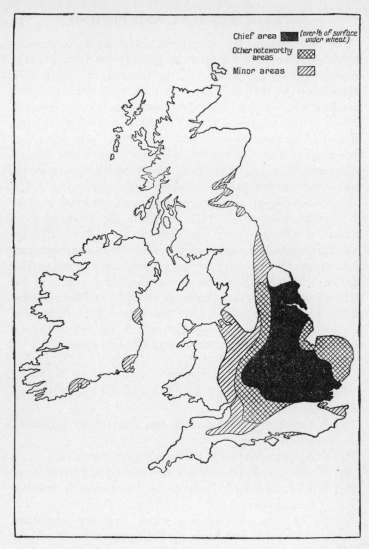

FIG. 18. WHEAT

Chief area ▓▓ (over⅛ of surface under wheat)
Other noteworthy areas ▨▨
Minor areas ▨

All these conditions are provided in eastern and south-eastern England, where the rainfall is less than thirty inches per annum, and the average July temperature over 60° F. The areas of chief production are the lowlands of midland and eastern England (see Fig. 18). Within this area counties where wheat-growing is of special importance are: Cambridge, Huntingdon, and the Holland district of Lincoln, where more than one-sixth of the land is under wheat. Since the outbreak of the Second World War the area specially important for wheat has been extended west and south to include such counties as Leicestershire, Oxfordshire, and Wiltshire.

Nearly all British wheat is sown in late autumn and has therefore a growing period of about ten months, a fact which, together with careful cultivation, accounts for the large yield per acre in contrast to the spring-sown wheats of Canada. Much of our wheat is, however, of the soft variety, and not very suitable for the making of bread, though it is excellent for mixing with the hard wheats from overseas.

BARLEY

There are several different types of barley, some of which require a dry climate while others will grow in fairly wet regions; but the only type which is really profitable in Britain is that used for the malt from which beer is made. As this type requires an even drier climate than wheat, the chief area of cultivation is the eastern portion of the wheat belt in East Anglia. Another reason for the concentration of barley in this area is that the crop does best on rather light sandy soils such as are found in certain parts of Norfolk.

FIG. 19. BARLEY

OATS

Oats will thrive in a cooler, damper climate than wheat or malting barley, though they also grow well in areas suited to the latter crops. They are therefore practically the only cereals grown on the wetter, western side of the country, and in the cooler northern parts, while in eastern England they compete with other cereals. The chief areas of production are the eastern coastal plain of Scotland, the lowland parts of Ulster, and the East Riding of Yorkshire. In England and Ireland nearly all the crop of oats is fed to farm animals, but in Scotland much is used for human food.

POTATOES

Potatoes are grown practically all over the British Isles, but they are of paramount importance in Ireland. In the Irish Republic the average crop is sufficient to provide every person with seven pounds of potatoes per day, while even in Northern Ireland, where the proportion of town-dwellers is very much larger, the crop would provide more than two pounds per head. It is obvious, therefore, that although potatoes are a staple food of the Irish people, there is still a very large surplus, which amounts, in fact, to far more than half the total crop. Most of this surplus is used as food for the farm animals, and is eventually marketed in the form of bacon.

In Great Britain areas which specialize in the production of potatoes as a 'money' crop are: the Holland district of Lincolnshire, the Isle of Ely (the northern part of Cambridgeshire), the district around Ormskirk in Lancashire, and southwestern Scotland. Scotland also specializes in the production

FIG. 20. OATS

of seed potatoes, since experience has shown that English farmers and gardeners get the best results by using Scotch seed potatoes. The most southerly districts of the British Isles, where the spring is earlier and warmer, specialize in the cultivation of early potatoes. Noteworthy areas are Cornwall and the Channel Isles.

MARKET GARDENING

In all the fairly densely peopled parts of the country there are to be found many gardeners and smallholders who earn a living by cultivating fruit, vegetables, flowers, and plants for sale in the shops and market-places of the neighbouring towns. In certain districts, however, such market gardening is the means of livelihood of a very large proportion of the population. Such specialization has in every case been determined by the operation of one or more of the following factors:

(1) The proximity of large towns, which provide a ready market.

(2) Light sandy soils, which are easily worked and which warm up quickly in spring, thus promoting the rapid growth of plants. This latter factor is a very important one, since vegetables, fruit, and flowers which are ready before the main crops from other districts have glutted the markets bring a considerably higher profit to the producer.

(3) A specially favourable climate, with mild winters, early springs, and abundant sunshine.

Proximity to the London market has been the chief factor determining the development of market gardening in the Lea valley, southern Essex, the Medway valley, and eastern Kent, though the actual location of the market gardens in these areas has been largely determined by special local conditions of soil, etc. In Kent, for example, it is found that the market gardeners avoid the low valley bottoms because on still, clear winter nights the heavy, cold air rolls down to the low-lying land, which is, therefore, more subject to frost than are the gentle slopes.

Light, sandy soils, abundant sunshine, and a rapid railway service to the great centres of population account for the success of market gardening in certain parts of the Fenland of eastern England, in the Vale of Evesham, and in the Hampshire basin, while the relatively high temperatures and early spring of Cornwall have given special facilities for the production of early vegetables.

FRUIT-GROWING

Home-grown fruits may be divided into two classes: small fruits, which include strawberries, raspberries, gooseberries, black currants, etc.; and orchard fruits, such as apples, pears, cherries, and plums. The fruit-growing industry, and especially the cultivation of small fruits, may be regarded as a specialized branch of market gardening, though in both cases the areas of commercial production are much more restricted than is the case with market gardening proper.

In England there are four areas where small fruits are of outstanding importance. These are: Kent, the Fenland around Wisbech, the lower Severn valley, and the Hampshire basin.

In Scotland, Blairgowrie, to the north of Perth, and the Carse of Gowrie on the northern side of the Tay estuary are specially noted for the cultivation of raspberries.

Kent, the lower Severn valley, and Somerset and Devon are the chief orchard areas, the first two specializing in apples and pears for eating, and the last-named counties in apples for the manufacture of cider.

The Fishing Industry

The British fishing fleet is by far the largest and best equipped in the world, and the value of fish landed at our ports is greater than that landed in any other country in the world, with the possible exception of Japan.

The factors which have favoured this great development of the industry are:

(1) The existence of the continental shelf, which, as already explained, provides excellent feeding-grounds for the fish and also facilitates the work of the fishermen.

(2) The large industrial population which forms the 'market' for most of the fish.

(3) The tidal currents and the Gulf Stream, which bring constant supplies of fish food to our shallow seas, and also help to cause the variations in temperature and salinity which make our seas suitable for different types of fish.

(4) The numerous inlets, which provide suitable harbours for the fishing vessels.

(5) The national aptitude for the sea, which seems to have been inherited from our Anglo-Saxon and Danish forefathers.

Our chief food fishes are divided into two classes—Pelagic fish, which live near the surface; and Demersal fish, which live on or near the sea-bed. Our chief pelagic fishes are the herring, sprat, mackerel, and pilchard. These are caught by drift-nets, which float vertically in the water, about ten feet below the surface. A herring fishing vessel, or drifter, may lay down in a night as much as ten miles of drift-netting, and the total catch of a good day's fishing at one of the large herring ports of England may amount to over twenty million fish.

The herring are caught as they swim inshore to spawn, and

as herrings of different types spawn at different times and places, the herring fishing season varies according to the locality. One type appears off the Hebrides in May, another

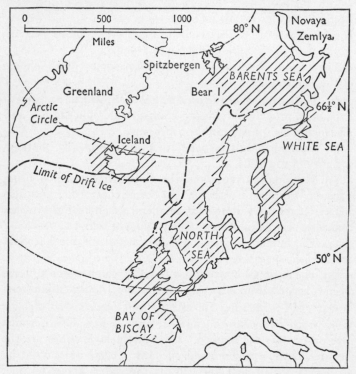

FIG. 21. NORTH-WEST EUROPE: FISHING-GROUNDS

type off the Orkneys and Shetlands in June, the Yorkshire and Lincolnshire coasts have their chief shoals in June and July, East Anglia in October, and Devon and Cornwall in December. The herring fishing fleets visit the various fishing-grounds in turn, the Scottish fleets coming as far south as Lowestoft. The herrings which formerly appeared in great shoals in the western part of the English Channel in December have now almost disappeared from that region. Such changes in the spawning grounds of the fish are due to variations in the amount of plankton in the surface waters.

A considerable proportion of the total catch of herrings is salted for export, the chief markets being the U.S.S.R. and Italy. Bloaters are prepared by salting and lightly smoking the whole fish, while kippers are herrings which have been split open and more thoroughly smoked.

Demersal fish, which include cod, halibut, haddock, whiting, plaice, and sole, are caught by trawls, seines, and lines. The trawl-net is a wide-mouthed tapering bag, which is pulled along the bed of the sea by the steam trawler. The seine is a similar net which is attached to a long line, one end of which is fastened to a buoy, and the other end to the trawler. After the seine has been paid out the vessel returns to the buoy, and the rope is wound in by means of motor winches. As the rope is dragged along the bottom it disturbs the fish and drives them towards the seine-net. Lines are used chiefly for such fish as cod and halibut, which are too large to be caught by nets. This method is predominant in Norwegian waters and on the Newfoundland Banks, but is now of little importance in British seas.

The chief fishing-grounds frequented by British vessels are shown in Fig. 21. Among the different types of fish landed at British ports, the chief, in respect of both weight and value, is cod, which is caught mainly in arctic waters and in the northern part of the North Sea. Halibut and haddock are other cold-water fishes which are caught in the northern seas, while hake is found chiefly off the south-western shores of Ireland. The chief catches of plaice are obtained from the Dogger Bank and the White Sea, while the sole is found chiefly in the southern part of the North Sea, in the Bristol Channel, the Bay of Biscay, and off the shores of Morocco.

Among the fishing ports the chief in order of weight of fish landed are: Grimsby, Hull, Yarmouth, Aberdeen, Lowestoft,

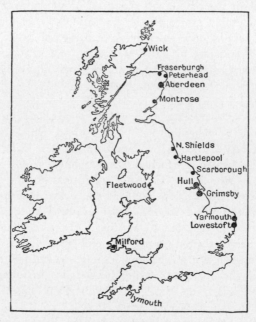

FIG. 22. FISHING PORTS

and Fleetwood. Of these only Yarmouth and Lowestoft are very important for herring, the rest being chiefly concerned with the dispatch of various types of fresh fish to the home markets. Most of the herrings are landed at small ports such as Fraserburgh and Peterhead, which specialize in the preparation of the fish for export and so do not need specially good railway connection to inland markets.

EXAMINATION QUESTIONS

1. What facts about the climate of the British Isles are illustrated by the figures in the accompanying table?

RAINFALL AT CERTAIN STATIONS

Station	Av. Annl. In.	Altitude Ft.
Gravesend	20·4	24
Dublin	27·7	54
Wick	29·9	81
Barrow	38·1	36
Valentia I. (S.W. Ireland) . .	56·0	12
Cambridge	22·1	35
The Stye (Cumberland) . .	176·9	1,070
Plynlimon	94·0	1,740
Arrochar (Loch Long) . .	91·8	50
Ben Nevis	162·6	4,407

(L. M.)

2. Discuss the advantages and disadvantages which Great Britain possesses as (*a*) a wheat-growing country; (*b*) a cattle-raising country.

(L. M.)

3. What is meant by 'sea-level isotherms'? Explain why sea-level isotherms showing the mean January temperatures in the British Isles run from north to south, but those for July run from east to west. (D. M.)

4. Describe the importance of tides in British seas in relation to (*a*) coastal land forms; (*b*) shipping; (*c*) the fishing industry. (D. M.)

5. By means of diagrams, show the types of weather we may expect in the British Isles when they are under the influence of:

　　(*a*) a high-pressure system;
　　(*b*) a low-pressure system.

Explain your diagrams. (D. S. C.)

6. In January the warmest parts of the British Isles are south-west Ireland and south-west England. In July the warmest area is south-east England. Account fully for these facts, using diagrams where necessary. (D. M.)

7. The following climatic data are those of certain places in the British Isles. Suggest the place or region to which you think each group of data belongs, and give full reasons for your answer.

	Temperature		Rainfall
	Coldest month	Hottest month	(Annual)
A.	44·3° F. (Feb.)	58·9° F. (Aug.)	55·6 in.
B.	38·9° F. (Jan.)	62·7° F. (July)	24·5 in.
C.	38·8° F. (Feb.)	56·9° F. (July)	80·4 in.

(D. M.)

8. Soil and climate affect the nature of the use of any area of lowland. Show that you appreciate this fact by describing clearly two different types of agriculture practised in the British Isles.

(D. M.)

9. What do you understand by a continental shelf? Illustrate your answer by comparing western Europe with some other area which is very different in this respect. (W. M.)

10. Describe the position of the British Isles. State the chief effects of this position on (a) British climate; (b) British commercial sea-routes. (N. U.)

11. Compare as fully as you can the climates of south-western Ireland and south-eastern England, and give reasons for the differences between them. (N. U.)

12. Examine the following figures:

X. 1·7, 1·4, 1·4, 1·5, 1·6, 1·4, 2·1, 1·8, 2·5, 3·1, 2·6, 2·2

Y. 3·8, 3·1, 3·2, 2·4, 2·6, 3·0, 3·8, 3·3, 3·7, 4·2, 5·0, 4·0

Z. 1·2, 1·0, 1·2, 1·4, 2·0, 2·0, 2·9, 2·9, 2·5, 1·7, 1·7, 1·7

They represent the monthly averages of rainfall in inches from January to December for two towns, X and Y, in the British Isles, and one town, Z, on the continent of Europe. X and Y are at sea-level, and Z about 500 ft. above sea-level. Point out any striking features of the figures, and suggest causes for the differences. Suggest also the localities of the three towns. (L. M.)

13. Compare the summer and winter climates of the west of Scotland (Clyde area) and the south of England (Hampshire area). Account for important differences. (L. M.)

14. Britain is said to stand on a continental shelf. What is meant by that statement? Explain why it is advantageous to Britain to be thus situated. What other European countries share in this advantage? (L. M.)

15. Account for the prevailing south-westerly winds in the British Isles. What difference would it make if the prevailing winds were south-easterly? (L. M.)

16. Contrast the summer and winter temperatures of the west of Scotland with those of the east of England. Account for differences, and point out results. (L. M.)

17. Account for the differences of rain distribution in the belt of land lying between the mouths of the Rivers Mersey, Clyde, Forth, and Humber. (L. G. S.)

18. 'An anticyclone is centred off our north-west coasts, while a depression is situated over the southern part of the North Sea.' Illustrate the above statement in map form. Mark with a liberal use of arrows the wind system that would be set up. Select a place where the weather would be dry and a place where it would be wet, giving reasons for your choice. (D. S. C.)

19. Name *one* area in the British Isles which is important for each of the following respectively: sheep-farming, dairy-farming, wheat-growing.
Describe the geographical conditions which help to determine the type of farming ascribed by you to each of the areas named.
(N. U.)

20. 'The distribution of sheep, cattle, and cereals in the British Isles is an index to the existing climatic conditions.' Explain this statement, and give examples in proof of it. (L. M.)

CHAPTER III

THE HIGHLANDS AND LOWLANDS OF
NORTHERN ENGLAND

NORTHERN ENGLAND may be said to be that portion of the
country which lies north of the Trent and the Dee. It

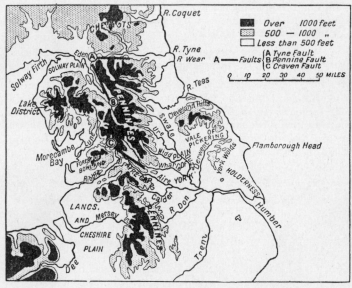

FIG. 23. NORTHERN ENGLAND—PHYSICAL

includes, therefore, not only the six so-called northern counties
—Northumberland, Durham, Yorkshire, Cumberland, West-
morland, and Lancashire—but also Cheshire and Derbyshire,
and the major portions of Staffordshire and Nottinghamshire.

The backbone of this great natural region is the Pennine Highland, which stretches from near the Scottish border to the Peak District of Derbyshire. This highland mass is often termed the Pennine *Chain*, but the term is misleading since the area does not consist of a chain of peaks, but is rather a dissected plateau.

The Pennine Highland is divided into three sections by great faults which run roughly from east to west.

THE NORTHERN PENNINES

The Northern Pennines lie between the Tyne Fault and the Stainmore Pass, which is followed by the Greta, a

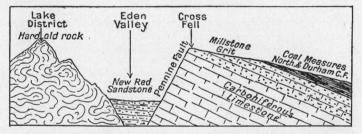

FIG. 24. DIAGRAMMATIC SECTION ACROSS NORTHERN ENGLAND

tributary of the Tees. As shown in Fig. 24, this section consists of a great block which dips gently towards the east, while on the west it is bounded by the great fault scarp overlooking the Vale of Eden and culminating in Cross Fell. The rocks of which the plateau are composed are infertile shale, sandstone, and limestone, and most of the surface consists of barren moors and poor pasture, which can be used only for sheep-rearing. The deep valleys or dales of north Yorkshire, such as Swaledale and Wensleydale (the valley of the Ure), are notable dairy-farming areas.

THE CENTRAL PENNINES

The Central Pennines lie between the Stainmore Pass and the Craven Fault, and are composed chiefly of a thick, almost horizontal layer of carboniferous limestone (so called because it belongs to the same series of rocks as the coal-measures) with a thin capping of sandstone and

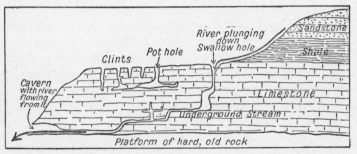

FIG. 25. DIAGRAM SHOWING FEATURES OF 'KARST' SCENERY

shale. Over the greater part of the area the capping has been worn away, leaving extensive platforms of almost pure limestone. It is in this region, therefore, that we find the finest examples of the *karst* type of scenery, which owes its characteristics to the fact that limestone, like chalk, is dissolved by rain-water. Naturally, the solvent action has proceeded most rapidly along the joints and lines of weakness in the rocks. Consequently, in many places the surface consists of 'clints' or detached blocks of limestone, separated by deep and narrow crevices following the joints. No surface-water is to be seen on the limestone plateaus, for the streams which flow over the remnants of the shale and the sandstone capping disappear gradually down water-sinks, or plunge down deep swallow-holes, as soon as they reach the limestone outcrop. One of the most remarkable swallow-holes is Gaping Ghyll, a well-like abyss on the flank of Ingleborough, where a small stream of the Lune basin falls for 365 feet to a subterranean cavern which is said to be the seventh largest in the world. The underground drainage of the limestone area has been investigated by the aid of powerful but harmless dyes, and many interesting facts have been brought to light. It has been shown, for example, that the underground streams do not always follow the dry surface valleys, in which they presumably flowed ages ago, but often take winding courses and emerge at quite unexpected places. In some cases streams are known to cross each other at different levels, and a stream which disappears on one side of a main valley may reappear on the opposite side, after passing under the river in the valley bottom.

Another interesting feature of the 'karst' country is the prevalence of caves, such as the famous Victoria Cave at Settle, in which the remains of prehistoric man have been found, or the White Scar Cavern at Ingleton, from which an underground passage runs to a beautiful lake in the very heart of the mountain.

THE SOUTHERN PENNINES

The Southern Pennines, which lie to the south of the Craven Fault and the Aire Gap, have already been described as a denuded arch (see Fig. 26). On the borders of Lancashire and Yorkshire the surface rock is *millstone grit*, a coarse, yellowish-brown sandstone which gets its name from the fact that it was formerly used for the millstones in flour mills. In this section are many deep, well-wooded valleys, above which rise the wide-spreading heather moors and peat bogs.

Farther south, in the Peak District of Derbyshire, the carboniferous limestone again comes to the surface and many of the features of the 'karst' country north of the Aire Gap are reproduced there.

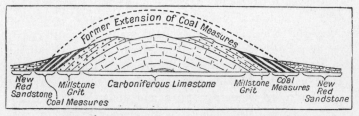

FIG. 26. SECTION ACROSS SOUTHERN PENNINES

The 'forests' of *Bowland* and *Rossendale*, on the Lancashire side of the main Pennine axis, consist chiefly of treeless moorland. The former is a thinly peopled pastoral area, but the latter is crossed by many densely peopled valleys, in which there are innumerable cotton factories, dye works, etc.

THE CUMBRIAN MOUNTAINS

The Cumbrian or Lake District Mountains differ from the Pennines in being formed of much harder and much older rocks which have been intensely folded. The processes of weathering, and the action of glaciers during the Great Ice Age, have carved out deep valleys, above which rise jagged peaks and knife-edge ridges which constitute some of the finest mountain scenery in the British Isles. As shown in Fig. 27, the valleys radiate from the centre like the spokes of a wheel, and almost every valley contains one or more lakes. These 'ribbon lakes,' as they are called on account of their shape, owe their origin to the action of the glaciers which

covered the land during the Great Ice Age. Some occupy
hollows scooped out by the glaciers, others are held up by

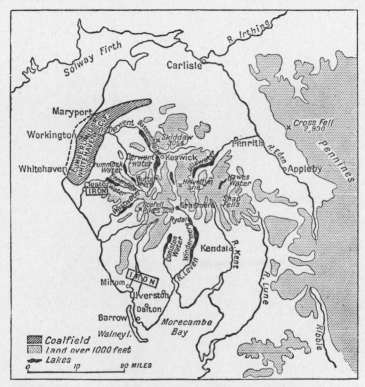

FIG. 27. LAKE DISTRICT AND THE CUMBERLAND COAL-FIELD

embankments of moraine deposited when the glaciers melted,
and some owe their origin to both these causes. Where two
lakes occupy the same valley, they are usually portions of a
pre-existing large lake which has been divided by the sediment
brought down by a side-stream and deposited in the form of

c

a delta. This is very clearly seen in the case of Derwentwater and Bassenthwaite, which are shown in Fig. 28.

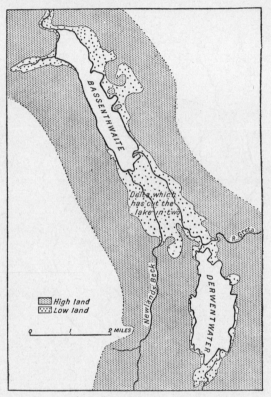

FIG. 28. DERWENTWATER AND BASSENTHWAITE

Communication within the Lake District is difficult, not only because the radial valleys are separated from each other by high mountains, but also because the central hub is of great height. Fortunately, the valley in which lie Windermere,

Rydal Water, and Grasmere is connected by the low pass of Dunmail Raise (782 feet high) with the valley containing Thirlmere, Derwentwater, and Bassenthwaite. Even this easy route across the Cumbrian Highland is not followed by a railway, but an excellent motor road gives easy communication between the northern and southern halves of the region. The only railway crossing the Lake District is the one from Workington through Keswick to Penrith. The low valleys used by this railway, together with the above-mentioned valley connecting Derwentwater and Windermere, divide the Lake District into three portions, each of which contains one of the highest peaks. In the northern sector lies Skiddaw (3,054 feet), in the western sector is Scafell Pike (3,210 feet), and in the eastern sector is Helvellyn (3,118 feet).

Despite the rugged nature of the land, pastoral farming is important. The mountain-slopes or fells are given up to the rearing of sheep of the Herdwick and other breeds which are hardy enough to live throughout the winter on the exposed mountain-sides. On the lower slopes are found mixed breeds which are less hardy but which fatten more readily and produce heavier fleeces.

Dairy farming is of considerable importance in the valleys, where the alluvial soil and the heavy rainfall favour the growth of good meadow grass. The climate is on the whole too wet for the cultivation of cereals, and the chief crops of the arable land of the valley floors are sown grasses and potatoes.

The mining industries are of little importance, though in the past small quantities of copper, lead, and graphite have been obtained. At the present time green roofing slate and granite are the only minerals produced in any quantity.

The beautiful scenery of the Lake District attracts great numbers of tourists and holiday-makers, and the tourist industry is one of the chief sources of livelihood for the people. Windermere, Ambleside, and Keswick are the largest of the tourist centres.

The York Moors and the Wolds

These low hills, which lie respectively in the North and East Ridings, belong structurally to south-eastern rather than to northern England, for they are extensions of the limestone and chalk ridges mentioned on page 9. The *York Moors*, with their northward extension, the Cleveland Hills, are part of the oolitic limestone belt, and consist of undulating, heather-clad moors, deeply dissected by fertile and picturesque valleys. Sheep-rearing and the raising of young cattle are the chief types of farming, though there is also a large proportion of ploughed land which is used chiefly to raise roots and cereals for the animals. The *Cleveland Hills* contain one of the largest deposits of iron ore in the British Isles, and though mining has fallen off considerably in recent years, the district still supplies about a million tons of ore per year.

The *York Wolds* are a continuation of the chalk scarps of south-eastern England, but as most of the surface is covered with glacial clay a large proportion of the land is under plough. The chief 'money' crops are malting barley and wheat, while root crops are grown as food for large flocks of sheep.

The Lowlands of Northern England

The *Lancashire and Cheshire Plain* lies between the Pennines and the west coast, and is crossed by the lower courses of the Rivers Lune, Ribble, Mersey, and Dee. It has already been pointed out that, on account of the moist, equable climate, dairying is the chief type of farming in the area, but market

Will F. Taylor

FLAMBOROUGH HEAD

gardening is important on reclaimed peaty land of Chat Moss between Manchester and Liverpool, while potatoes are the chief speciality of the plain around Ormskirk. The Fylde district between Blackpool and Preston is one of the chief poultry-farming areas in the world.

The *Solway Plain* and the *Vale of Eden* are important cattle-rearing areas, specializing in both stock-raising and milk production. Milk is dispatched daily to Glasgow, Edinburgh, and the industrial districts of Lancashire and the West Riding. The chief arable crops are oats, turnips, and rotation grass, all for stock feeding.

The *Plain of York*, which lies between the Pennines and the York Moors and York Wolds, has a drier and sunnier climate than the corresponding plain of Lancashire and Cheshire, and has consequently a larger proportion of wheat land. From the agricultural point of view the Plain of York is more like south-eastern than northern England. It is, for example, the most northerly area where wheat is a dominant crop. Large quantities of oats and barley are grown, and rotation grass and root-crops, including sugar beet, provide food for large numbers of dairy and beef cattle.

Though mixed farming predominates on the plain, there are interesting specializations in certain districts. In the lower, tidal portions of the Ouse and Derwent, land which was formerly subject to floods has been converted into rich arable land by the process of warping, which consists of building embankments to retain the muddy waters of the high tides until the silt has been deposited. The grasses which grow in the first deposits of silt help to collect more mud from successive high tides, and so hasten the process of building up new land. On such reclaimed land large crops of potatoes and sugar-beet are grown. In the northern portion of the plain, around Thirsk, there are deposits of light, sandy glacial soils which are devoted largely to the production of potatoes, carrots, and peas. The district around Leeds and Wakefield specializes in the production of rhubarb, nearly one-half of the total yield of the country coming from this area. Some liquorice is still grown around Pontefract, where it is manufactured into sweets.

York is situated in the middle of the plain, at the head of navigation of the Ouse, and on a slight ridge which provides a natural route across the plain from west to east. It has therefore been a route centre from the time of the Romans, who named the place Eboracum and made it their chief military station in the north. In modern times it has become an important railway centre, and is noted for flour-milling and the manufacture of chocolate.

The *Vale of Pickering* lies between the York Moors and the Wolds. The River Derwent, which now drains the vale southward to the Ouse, formerly ran eastward to enter the sea at Filey, but during the Ice Age this exit was blocked by a moraine, thus forming a great lake which was eventually drained by the present river cutting a deep gorge in the western lip of the basin. The mud which was deposited at the bottom of this former lake now forms the rich meadow land which occupies the flat bottom of the vale, while the slightly higher, drier land above the flood-level is largely arable.

Holderness is the low plain which lies between the Wolds, the Humber, and the North Sea coast. The seaward edge of the plain is gradually being worn away by waves, while new land is being formed by the deposition of sediment on the northern shore of the Humber. The low, hook-shaped peninsula of Spurn Head is a sand-spit which has been built up during the last 400 years and which is still gradually extending southward.

CHAPTER IV

INDUSTRIES OF THE YORK, DERBY, AND NOTTS. COAL-FIELD

In studying the industrial and commercial geography of this region it is convenient to divide it into four sections, viz.:

(1) The woollen-manufacturing district of the West Riding.
(2) The iron- and steel-manufacturing district around Sheffield.
(3) The textile and engineering district of the southern tip of the coal-field around Derby and Nottingham.
(4) The concealed coal-field and the Humber.

I. The West Riding Woollen-manufacturing District

Since the manufacture of woollen goods was the dominant industry of these islands from the thirteenth to the nineteenth centuries, its history epitomizes all the phases of industrial development during those centuries. Three principal stages of industrial organization may be recognized, though it must be understood that there was no sudden change from one to the other:

(a) The *Guild System*, which lasted from the twelfth to the end of the sixteenth century. Under this system production was chiefly in the hands of craftsmen who owned their own machinery, bought the raw materials, and sold the finished products. In each craft the workers were associated

55

in guilds, whose function it was to assist and protect the
members—masters, journeymen, and apprentices—and to

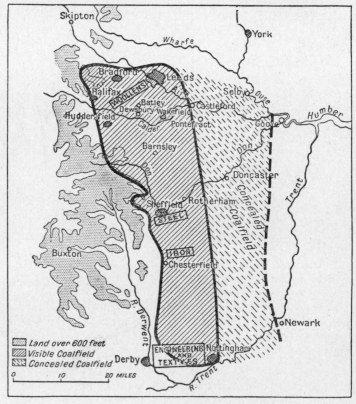

FIG. 29. YORK, DERBY, AND NOTTS. COAL-FIELD

maintain the honour of the craft by insisting on a high
standard of workmanship. As the output of manufactured
goods increased it became impossible for each craftsman to
market his own products, and so there arose a class of

middlemen or merchants, who gradually changed the organization of industry to

(*b*) The *Domestic System*, which began about the end of the sixteenth century and lasted till the latter half of the eighteenth century. Under this system the merchants bought the raw materials, paid the craftsmen for working them up, and marketed the finished product.

The manufacturing process was, however, carried on in the homes of the craftsmen, either by hand or by the aid of simple machines which they themselves owned. Under this system, however, the power of the guilds inevitably declined, and there was a natural tendency for the merchants to acquire the machines, and set up workshops or factories. Such development, though discouraged by both the craftsmen and the government, was hastened by the invention of machinery which required mechanical power. Thus the domestic system gradually gave place to

(*c*) The *Factory System*, which began about 1760, and developed rapidly as a result of the numerous inventions which characterized the Industrial Revolution.

During the Middle Ages, and so long as industry continued under the guild system, the West Riding was only a minor centre of the woollen industry, the chief centres being East Anglia and the West Country (Gloucester, Wiltshire, and Somerset). These areas, like the West Riding, had local supplies of wool, and streams of soft water for washing the wool, and had the further advantage of being situated in comparatively densely peopled areas, whereas the north of England was a thinly peopled area, with restricted local markets. With the development of the domestic system, however, the West Riding and the neighbouring parts of Lancashire rapidly increased in importance, largely because the guilds, which had never been well established in the north,

* c

hampered the expansion of the industry in other parts of the country. Thus the West Riding, even before the Industrial Revolution, had become the chief centre of the woollen industry.

Towards the end of the eighteenth century the machines which had been invented for use in the Lancashire cotton industry were introduced into Yorkshire, and many spinning-

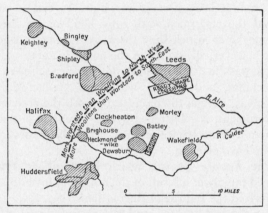

FIG. 30. THE WEST RIDING WOOLLEN DISTRICT

mills were built in the steep valleys of the Pennines, where there was abundant water-power. Weaving was, however, still largely done on hand looms in the homes, the finished 'pieces' being taken to cloth halls in Halifax, Bradford, and other towns, or to local warehouses owned by the spinners and merchants.

With the introduction of the steam-engine at the beginning of the nineteenth century the factories in the high valleys were abandoned, and large factory towns began to grow up in the broad valleys on the coal-field. During this period of development other centres of the industry rapidly declined, largely because of the lack of local coal supplies, and at the present time the West Riding employs about 80 per cent of all the workers in the woollen industry.

As shown in Fig. 30, the woollen-manufacturing area is almost restricted to the basins of the Calder and the northward-flowing tributaries of the Aire. Reasons why the industry has not expanded north of the Aire are: (1) The Aire is approximately the northern boundary of the coal-field. (2) Before wool can be spun it must be scoured or washed to remove the grease. For this purpose soft water is necessary, as hard water would be very wasteful of soap and chemicals. The streams south of the Aire flow from the sandstone moorlands and therefore contain soft water, while the upper Aire and its northern tributaries flow over limestone which makes the water hard.

SPECIALIZATION IN THE INDUSTRY

The woollen industry differs from the cotton industry in that there is no sharp division into weaving and spinning branches; on the contrary, both sections of the industry are carried on in the same towns, and very often by the same firms. There are, however, well-recognized divisions according to the quality of the raw materials and of the finished product.

Worsteds, which took their name from the village of Worstead in Norfolk, are high-quality cloths manufactured from the longer, finer fibres of wool, while *woollens* are manufactured from shorter, thicker, and less uniform fibres. Woollen fabrics, after being woven, are passed through rollers which cause the fibres to interlock or 'felt' so that individual threads cannot easily be seen in the finished cloth, whereas worsted fabrics are not felted, and the pattern of the weave can easily be traced. Though both worsted and woollen branches of the industry are carried on in all parts of the West Riding textile area, the portion south of a line joining Halifax to Leeds specializes to a greater extent in woollens than in worsteds, while the northern half is more noted for worsteds. *Shoddies*, which are made from yarn obtained by pulling to pieces rags, clippings, etc., are manufactured at Batley, Dewsbury, and several small towns in the Spen valley.

Carpets are manufactured from thick, short-fibred wools. The chief centre of the industry in the West Riding is Halifax.

Blankets, which are of course very heavily felted and belong therefore to the woollen branch of the industry, are made at Halifax, and at Rochdale in Lancashire. The survival of the industry in this latter town is a reminder of the fact that before the rise of the cotton industry woollen goods were manufactured on both sides of the Pennines.

Bradford, situated on a small northward-flowing tributary of the Aire, is the merchanting centre of both the worsted and the woollen branches of the industry, and at its Exchange manufacturers from all over the West Riding meet to arrange their business. The city is also a great centre for the spinning and weaving of worsteds and of fabrics made from mohair. Much artificial fibre, such as rayon and nylon, is also used.

Halifax, situated on a great dip slope on the northern side of the Calder valley, specializes in worsteds, as well as in heavy woollen goods such as carpets.

Huddersfield, situated at the convergence of several deep valleys tributary to the Calder, is noted for high-class suitings.

Leeds, though the largest town of the West Riding, is not specially concerned with the textile industry, though it has many woollen and worsted mills. It is, however, the chief centre in the country, and probably in the world, for factory-made clothing, about 20 per cent of the population being

engaged in the industry.   It is also noteworthy for the manufacture of wrought iron and textile machinery.   Other important industries are the manufacture of boots and shoes,
chemicals, and glass.   The city owes its rise chiefly to its
situation at the focus of routes northward and southward
along the edge of the Pennines, westward via the Aire and
Calder valleys, and eastward to the Humber.   Besides being
one of the chief road and railway centres of northern England,
it has some importance as a river port, as it is accessible by
steam barges from the Humber, and is served by the Aire and
Calder Navigation, which is the most prosperous of the barge
canals of Britain.

II. THE SOUTH YORKSHIRE IRON AND STEEL AREA

Sheffield was an important iron-manufacturing centre as
far back as the twelfth century, and has been famous for the
manufacture of steel for more than four hundred years.   The
reasons which led to the early development of the industry
in this area are:

(1) The occurrence of beds of iron ore so close to the
surface that they could be reached by quarries and bell pits.

(2) The abundance of timber for the making of charcoal,
which was used to smelt the iron ore before the Industrial
Revolution.

(3) The numerous deep, steep-sided valleys which provided
water-power for working the bellows which supplied blasts
of air to the furnaces, and for operating the tilt-hammers
used in beating out the iron.

(4) The occurrence of thick beds of millstone grit which is
suitable for the making of grindstones.

When coke replaced charcoal in the smelting process, the

Sheffield district was found to have large supplies of good coking coal, but none of the factors mentioned above is of importance to the modern steel industry. Even in the sixteenth century Swedish iron was used to the exclusion of the local product for the manufacture of the cutlery for which Sheffield was even then famous. At the present time pig iron is brought from Scunthorpe and Cleveland, and high quality Swedish bar iron is imported for the manufacture of special steels. Sheffield has some slight advantage over other coal-mining areas in having local supplies of ganister, a very hard sandstone used for lining furnaces, but it is to man rather than to nature that the city owes its present predominance in the steel industry. The early establishment of the industry created a reservoir of highly skilled labour; many of the processes which revolutionized the steel industry in the eighteenth and nineteenth centuries were either invented or brought to perfection in the local workshops; and during the present century discoveries by Sheffield steel manufacturers and research scientists have enabled the city to maintain her long-established predominance. The Sheffield steel industry is thus seen to be an excellent example of *geographical inertia*, or *commercial momentum*—terms which are used to describe the tendency for industries to be maintained in the area where they originally developed, even though the factors which caused the rise of those industries are no longer of importance.

At the present time two distinct branches of the Sheffield steel industry may be recognized, viz.: (*a*) the cutlery and light-steel industry which is centred on the higher land around the tributary river Sheaf; and (*b*) the heavy steel industry which is centred on the lower land around the Don.

One of the chief specialities of the industry at the present

time is the production of 'special steels,' which are made by
the addition of small quantities of other metals such as man-
ganese, nickel, and vanadium.

Rotherham, situated some six miles lower down the River
Don, makes special steels and heavy steel castings, but is also
famous for the manufacture of brassware and of domestic
grates, ranges, and other articles made of cast iron.

Chesterfield, situated some ten miles south of Sheffield, and
just within the borders of Derbyshire, specializes in the
manufacture of iron pipes for water- and gas-mains.

III. Nottingham and Derby

The industrial region served by the southern tip of the
York, Derby, and Notts. coal-field specializes in many industries, the chief of which are engineering and the manufacture of textiles. *Nottingham* grew up on a defensible site
near the head of navigation of the Trent, and around a castle
which guarded a suitable crossing place of the river. In
modern times its situation at the southern tip of the coal-
field, between the industrial north and the agricultural south-
east, has made it an important market town, while in recent
years the canalizing of the Trent has made it an important
river port.

The two characteristic industries of the city—the manufacture of lace and hosiery—owe their origin largely to local
inventions. In 1589 William Lee, a clergyman of Nottingham,
invented a machine for knitting stockings, and the industry
soon became firmly established in the district. Until the
latter part of the eighteenth century lace-making remained
a domestic industry, but about that time the stocking-frame
was adapted to the weaving of plain lace net, and in 1834

a machine was invented which could produce elaborate designs on the plain net. In recent years there has been a considerable decline in the demands for lace curtains, etc., but the industry is still dominant in the city, though the manufacture of 'knitwear,' including hosiery, has increased greatly in modern times.

Other important industries are associated with three world-famous firms, viz.: Raleigh (bicycles), Boots (drugs), and Players (cigarettes).

Derby is situated a few miles to the west of the coal-field, where the valley of the Derwent, which has always carried an important cross-Pennine route to Manchester, opens out to the Midland Plain.

Since Roman times, lead has been mined in the carboniferous limestone of the southern Pennines, and Derby was the chief distributing centre for the metal until modern times, when most of our lead began to be imported. Though some lead is still mined in Derbyshire, Derby is no longer noted as a marketing centre for the metal, though two industries in which lead is of use—the manufacture of paint and pottery —still survive.

The cotton industry was established near Derby by Arkwright, the inventor of the spinning-frame, and there are still many factories which specialize in the manufacture of 'small-wares' such as tape, braid, and elastic. The building of locomotives is an important industry, as the city was chosen by the Midland Railway as its chief engineering centre because of the proximity of coal and iron, and because of its central situation with regard to the railway system. Derby is also world famous as the home of the Rolls-Royce motor-car.

IV. The Concealed Coal-field

As shown in Figs. 29 and 31, there is between the Trent and the eastern edge of the visible coal-field a large area where the coal-seams are less than three thousand feet below the surface, and it is in this area that the chief expansion of the coal-mining industry is taking place. The centre of this new

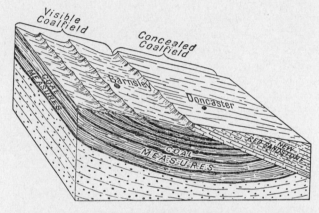

FIG. 31. BLOCK DIAGRAM SHOWING VISIBLE AND CONCEALED COAL-FIELDS

coal-field is *Doncaster*, a historic town which grew up near the natural head of navigation of the Don, and at the point where the Great North Road of coaching days crossed the river on its way to York. In modern times it first rose to importance as the chief engineering and locomotive-building centre of the L.N.E.R., and it is now of increasing importance as the market centre of the newly developed coal-field. Around it have grown up many well-planned mining villages which contrast strongly with the older villages and towns on the visible coal-field.

The Humber and its Ports

Hull is situated about twenty-five miles from the sea at the point where the little River Hull enters the Humber. (The full name of the city is Kingston-upon-Hull.)   In the

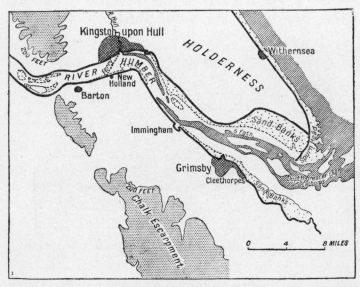

FIG. 32. HULL AND THE HUMBER

days of small vessels the port was not of great importance as nearly all the boats passed it by on the way to such inland ports as York, Gainsborough, and Selby; but as vessels became larger these ports decayed, and Hull rose into prominence. Strange as it may seem, it is to the shape of the Humber estuary that Hull owes its importance as a deep-water port. Observation of a winding river shows that the current clings to the outer. concave bank at every curve, and that the deepest water is to be found close to this bank. The sketch-map, Fig. 32, shows that this rule applies also to the Humber, and it is a fortunate coincidence that the River Hull enters the estuary at the westward end of the deep-water channel which clings to the outer bank of the curve. The first docks were made at the mouth of the smaller river, but later and larger docks extend for two miles east and west of the old harbour.

Though its immediate hinterland is only thinly peopled, Hull is the natural outlet for the York, Derby, and Notts. coal-field, the West Riding woollen district, the Sheffield steel area, and the Notts. and Derby textile and engineering region, and now ranks as the third port of Britain in respect of the total value of its trade. It is not, however, specially noted for the import of the raw materials required by these industrial areas; in particular it should be noted that only about one-seventh of the wool imported by Britain enters the country via Hull, whereas London imports nearly half the total, and Liverpool more than one-fifth. The reason for the predominance of London is that, as the long-established wool market of the world, it is able to offer facilities for storing, classing, and selling which cannot be equalled by any other port. Liverpool has also some advantage over Hull in that it is the home port for many lines of steamers trading with Australia, South Africa, and South America. Much of the wool imported via London is, however, after-wards sent by coastal steamer to Hull, so the total amount of wool handled by the port is much greater than that shown by the figures for the imports, which do not include coastal traffic.

The leading imports of Hull are foodstuffs, such as wheat, butter, bacon, and eggs, which are distributed to the in-dustrial areas of the West Riding, timber, pit-props, and con-structional timber from Scandinavia, Finland, and Russia, and oil seeds such as linseed and soya beans. These imports have given rise to the characteristic industries of the port—flour-milling, and the manufacture of vegetable oils which in their turn are the raw material for the manufacture of paint, while the residue is pressed into cattle cake.

The exports of Hull are valued at only 40 per cent of the imports, and consist chiefly of manufactured goods from Yorkshire, Lancashire, and the Midlands.

Hull is also one of the chief fishing ports of the world, most of her fishing vessels being large trawlers which work in the distant fishing-grounds near Iceland and the White Sea.

Goole, situated near the confluences of the Don and the Aire with the Ouse, has the advantage of being nearer than Hull to the industrial areas, but the disadvantage of being accessible only by small steamers. One of the chief commodities dealt with is coal, much of which is brought to it by the 'compartment boats'—trains of rectangular containers drawn by tugs—which ply on the canals and canalized rivers of the Aire and Calder Navigation system.

Grimsby grew up around a small inlet on the southern side of the Humber. It is the world's chief fishing port, but it owes this distinction chiefly to the construction of railways which were built to connect it with the densely peopled districts of the West Riding and the Midlands. Like Hull, it imports dairy produce and timber.

Immingham is another port which owes its rise to the construction of railways. It is situated where the current swings close to the southern bank of the Humber, and was chosen in 1912 by the Great Central Railway (later part of the L.N.E.R.) as the most suitable site for a new deep-water port. It is concerned chiefly with the shipping of coal to London and the import of timber.

CHAPTER V

INDUSTRIES OF NORTHERN ENGLAND (*contd.*)

The North-Eastern Industrial Area

THIS region, which lies between the north Pennines, the North Sea coast, and the North York Moors, includes the Northumberland and Durham coal-field and the iron-working and chemical manufacturing district of Tees-side.

The Northumberland and Durham coal-field has for many centuries been specially concerned with the shipment of coal to London, and records show that even as early as the fourteenth century 'sea cole' was sent from the Tyne to London. The reasons for this early development of the shipment of coal in this area are:

(1) Coal-seams outcropped on the coast and in the mouths of the rivers, so that, with the aid of 'staithes,' or wooden platforms built out from the shore, coal could be loaded directly into the vessels.

(2) The coal-field is crossed by many deep valleys, and the coal could easily be mined by means of tunnels driven into the valley sides.

(3) As the seams near the coast became exhausted, various devices were adopted to facilitate transport between the more distant mines and the ships. The first improvement upon the muddy tracks usable only by pack-horses were 'corduroy' roads made of logs; then wooden rails were used; and these finally gave way to iron rails. For a time the

wagons on such 'railways' were pulled by horses, but in 1825 the era of steam locomotion was inaugurated by the opening of the Stockton and Darlington Railway, on which ran George Stephenson's famous Number One engine. Within a few decades railways were built from various parts of the coal-field to ports on the Rivers Tyne, Wear, and Tees, thus making possible an enormously increased output of coal.

As the coal-seams dip eastward from the flanks of the Pennines, most of the large mines are situated in the eastern half of the coal-field, where they have the advantage of nearness to the sea, and where the shafts pass through several seams. In south-eastern Durham the coal-seams are hidden under thick layers of newer rock, but it is in this concealed coal-field that most of the mining is now carried on.

THE IRON AND STEEL INDUSTRY

Even in Roman times some mining and smelting of iron was done in the north-eastern district, but the supplies of coal-measure ore were never large, and it was not until the middle of last century that any great development of the industry took place. In 1850 a thick bed of iron ore was discovered in the Cleveland Hills, and Tees-side—i.e. the district around the estuary of the river—rapidly rose to preeminence as an iron-smelting and manufacturing area. By 1860 Cleveland was yielding nearly half the total production of the United Kingdom, while Middlesbrough, which in 1830 was a small village with less than 200 inhabitants, had within a century a population of 138,000.

The factors which favoured the rapid growth of the iron and steel industries in this area are:

(1) The occurrence of a thick bed of iron ore within ten miles of the navigable estuary of the Tees.

(2) The occurrence of excellent coking coal in the neighbouring concealed coal-field of south Durham.

(3) Ample supplies of limestone, which is needed for smelting, in the Pennines and in the valley of the Wear.

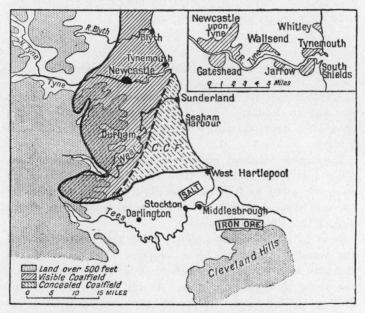

FIG. 33. THE NORTH-EASTERN INDUSTRIAL AREA

(4) The navigability of the Tees estuary, which facilitates the import of foreign ores richer in iron than that of Cleveland.

(5) The enormous demand during the nineteenth century for steel railway lines and for iron and steel ships for carrying the coal sent out by sea from the Northumberland and Durham coal-field.

The whole north-eastern region, from Tyne to Tees, produces about a quarter of the iron and steel of the country, though only a small part of the ore used is now mined in the Cleveland district. Much high-grade ore is imported from Sweden and northern Africa, and large quantities are also brought from Lincolnshire and Northamptonshire.

THE TOWNS AND MANUFACTURING INDUSTRIES

Middlesbrough has already been mentioned as an important iron and steel centre. It is also a great engineering centre, its most notable speciality being the manufacture of steel bridges.

Stockton is situated on the opposite bank of the Tees, about four miles higher up the river and at the head of sea navigation, but as it is not accessible by large steamers its overseas trade is small. It is a general engineering centre and a minor shipbuilding centre.

Near by is *Billingham-on-Tees*, where are situated some of the world's largest chemical factories. The basis of the chemical industry is salt which is obtained by pumping up the brine through bore-holes. As on the estuary of the Mersey, the chemical industry has grown up on a navigable waterway, near both salt and coal. At *Wilton*, on the south bank of the Tees, a great new chemical plant has recently been built for the 'cracking' of petroleum and for the manufacture of terylene and other synthetic products.

The Hartlepools consist of the older town of Hartlepool, and the larger, more modern town of *West Hartlepool*. The latter is an important industrial centre, its chief industries being shipbuilding, engineering, and the manufacture of paper and sailcloth. As a port it is notable for the dispatch of coal to

London and the importation of timber, especially the pit-props needed by the coal-field.

Darlington, situated a few miles north of the Tees in the gateway between the Pennines and the North York Moors, owed its early development to the railway which linked it to Stockton, while in modern times it is notable chiefly as a railway engineering centre.

Sunderland, situated at the mouth of the River Wear, is the largest town of the county of Durham. The River Wear is not navigable, and it was only with great difficulty that even the lowest five miles of the estuary were deepened sufficiently to accommodate large vessels, but the position of Sunderland at the junction of the zone of older mines on the visible coal-field with the area of newer and larger pits on the concealed coal-field has given it a great advantage as a coal port. One large colliery is situated in the very heart of the town, and within half a mile of the staithes from which the coal is shipped. The demand for ships created by the coal trade, the proximity of coal, and the nearby supplies of steel, have given rise to the shipbuilding industry, and in normal times the town ranks next to Clydeside and Tyneside in respect of the tonnage of ships launched. The associated industry of marine engineering is also of great importance, and most of the vessels launched on the Wear are fitted with engines made in the local workshops.

Seaham Harbour, situated some five miles to the south of Sunderland, is a good example of a port founded for a single purpose—in this case the distribution of coal from the south Durham coal-field.

Newcastle has become the most important town of the region because of the natural advantages of its position. It is situated at the lowest suitable bridge place on the Tyne, where high ground approaches both banks of the river, and was for that reason selected by the Romans as a fortress at the end of Hadrian's Wall which followed the Tyne Gap. The Normans built a 'new castle' there to guard the route into Scotland, and the building of the first bridge made it the normal head of navigation, though until comparatively recent times the estuary was so shallow that coal for export had to be taken to the mouth of the river in light draught vessels known as keels, there to be transferred to sea-going ships.

In modern times the estuary has been deepened by dredging so that Newcastle is accessible by vessels drawing thirty feet of water. Its chief exports are coal, coke, ships, machinery, and iron and steel goods. It is, however, even more important as the business capital of a manufacturing region than as a port. The outstanding industry of Tyneside is shipbuilding, and the narrow strips of lowland on each side of the river from Newcastle to the mouth are occupied with shipyards and engineering shops. Many of the world's largest battleships have been built on the Tyne, as well as some large ocean liners, as well as innumerable smaller craft such as tramp steamers and oil-tankers.

Gateshead, situated on the southern side of the river opposite to Newcastle, and connected with it by four bridges, is an engineering centre and also manufactures chemicals, glass, and cement.

Wallsend and *Jarrow*, situated respectively north and south of the river, and about midway between Newcastle and the sea, are engaged chiefly in shipbuilding and marine engineering. *Tynemouth*, a county borough which includes *North Shields*, is especially noted for ship repairing and is also the most important fishing port of the north-east coast, while *South Shields*, on the opposite side of the river, has several shipyards, and also manufactures glass and chemicals.

Blyth, situated eight miles north of the Tyne, shipped coal to London as early as the thirteenth century, but its importance as a modern coal port dates only from the end of the last century.

CHAPTER VI

NORTHERN ENGLAND (*contd.*)

I. The Cotton Industry of Lancashire

The cotton-manufacturing area of south-east Lancashire, with the neighbouring fringes of west Yorkshire and north Cheshire, contains about 85 per cent of the cotton operatives of the British Isles and a large, though decreasing, proportion of the world's spindles and cotton looms. The reasons for the development and concentration of the industry in this area may be summarized as follows:

(1) For many centuries previous to the introduction of cotton, the people had been engaged in the manufacture of woollen and linen goods under the domestic system.

(2) In medieval times the present cotton towns were not subject to the restrictions which were imposed by the guilds in many parts of the country, and so were free to adopt new methods.

(3) In the seventeenth century Flemish refugees settled in the Manchester district, and probably introduced the art of spinning and weaving cotton.

(4) Most of the great inventions of spinning and weaving machinery were made in Lancashire. Among these may be mentioned Kay's flying shuttle, Hargreaves's spinning-jenny, and Cartwright's power loom.

(5) The numerous rapid streams, which in the early

days of the Industrial Revolution provided power for the machines.

(6) The abundance of coal, which, after the invention of the steam-engine, rapidly replaced water as a source of power.

(7) The ample supplies of soft water from the moorland streams, which aided the development of the bleaching and dyeing branches of the industry.

(8) The intersection of the uplands by numerous deep valleys, which facilitated the construction of canals, roads, and railways.

(9) The presence of a good port, Liverpool, conveniently situated for the importation of raw cotton from the United States, Egypt, and, in former times, India.

(10) The damp climate, which makes it easier to spin and weave the finer threads of cotton. It is said that the Lancashire cotton operative can detect when the wind changes from west to east by the greater frequency with which the 'ends' of cotton threads break. This factor of humidity is not, however, of great importance in modern times, since artificial humidifiers are used to create suitable humid conditions even in dry areas.

The organization of the Lancashire cotton industry differs from that of the Yorkshire woollen industry, in that the spinning and weaving are not usually conducted in the same factory, or even in the same district. Most of the spinning is done in a group of towns which form a crescent to the north and east of Manchester and some ten or twelve miles distant from it. The chief of these spinning towns are Bolton, Rochdale, and Oldham. The first-named town specializes in the spinning of fine yarn from high-quality cotton, while the last two spin chiefly the coarser types of yarn. All the spinning towns are also engaged in weaving, but on the northern edge of the coal-field is a line of towns—Preston,

Blackburn, Accrington, Burnley, Nelson, and Colne—which specialize in weaving only and conduct little spinning. It is, indeed, a remarkable fact that within the cotton district, the

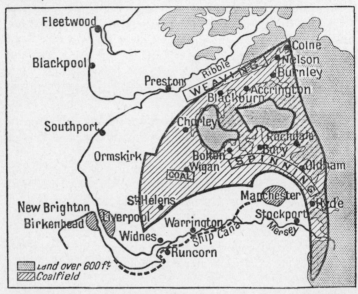

FIG. 34. THE LANCASHIRE COTTON-
MANUFACTURING DISTRICT

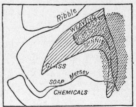

FIG. 35. KEY DIAGRAM AS
BASIS OF SKETCH-MAP OF
LANCASHIRE

farther one gets from Manchester, which is the marketing and organizing centre of the industry, the fewer spinning mills and the more weaving factories one sees.

The chief reason for the separation of the industry into two distinct branches, spinning and 'manufacturing' (i.e. weaving), is that the manufacturer or weaving-master requires such a large variety of yarn that he finds it cheaper and more convenient to buy his stocks from the various spinning mills which specialize in the particular grades he may require for a given type of cloth, rather than to install spinning machinery which could only turn out a few grades of yarn. Even so, it is difficult to understand why the weaving industry has gravitated to the northern edge of the coal-field, and why the spinning mills are concentrated in the towns near to Manchester. Neither is it easy to explain, from a geographical point of view, why certain weaving towns specialize in particular types of cloth. Thus Preston specializes in the manufacture of shirting and high-quality cloth, Blackburn in cheap, thin cloth for the tropics Burnley in cloth for printing, Nelson and Colne in various types of patterned cloth.

Bleaching, printing, dyeing, and finishing represent a third branch of the cotton industry, for these processes are seldom carried out by either the spinning or weaving firms. Since one of the chief requisites for these processes is an abundant supply of pure soft water, the factories are found chiefly in the valleys of the Rossendale Forest, where they have the further advantages of being near to both weaving and spinning centres, as well as to Manchester, the great market and warehousing centre.

Before the First World War Lancashire had no serious rival in the world's cotton market, but in modern times many countries which formerly imported their cotton goods from Britain have set up cotton factories of their own, and aided by excellent organization and by the fact that their people are willing to work for low wages, have enormously increased their production of cotton goods. Britain has thus been almost ousted from some of her former markets for the cheaper cotton goods. Nevertheless, high quality cotton goods still provide one of our most valuable exports. In recent years there has been a great increase in the use of rayon and other artificial fibres in place of cotton.

Coal-mining. The Lancashire coal-field has been worked from very early times, and the output is not now sufficient to meet the needs of the county, considerable quantities being brought into the district from Yorkshire. The chief coal-mining areas are in the south-east around Manchester, and in the south-west around Wigan, while the Burnley area has many small mines. The coal-field produces only about 6 per cent of the country's total output.

Slipper manufacture. This industry is concentrated at the small town of Waterfoot in the Rossendale valley, where it grew up as a result of the establishment of the manufacture of felt. It was the custom for the workmen in this latter industry to make for themselves slippers of felt for use at their work, and during a period of depression in the cotton industry a few families began to manufacture felt slippers on a wholesale scale. The industry was so successful that the annual output is now about twenty million pairs a year.

Manchester first grew up around a fortress which was situated at the focus of valley tracks and protected by the marshes of the Irwell and by the small tributary stream, the Medlock. It did not, however, become of great importance until the rise of the textile industry. Then its situation at the focus of the valley routes across the Rossendale highland made it the natural marketing centre even before the Industrial Revolution. With the development of the Lancashire cotton industry, and the building of canals, roads, and railways with Manchester as their centre, the population of the city increased from 15,000 in 1729, when the first Exchange was built, to 150,000 in 1820. Now it has a population of nearly three-quarters of a million, while within a radius of fifteen miles from the centre of the city are approximately 2,500,000 people.

The importance of the city is due primarily to its function as the marketing and business centre for the Lancashire cotton-manufacturing area, and the business quarters are occupied principally by the offices and warehouses of cotton merchants and manufacturers whose works are situated on the coal-field to the north and east.

Salford, Manchester's twin town on the opposite side of the Irwell, has a population of 175,000, and is an industrial centre engaged chiefly in all branches of the cotton industry, engineering, and the manufacture of waterproof clothing.

Manchester-Salford is, however, not only a manufacturing and commercial centre, but also one of the world's chief ports. The Manchester Ship Canal, which was opened in 1894, runs from Eastham Lock, near the mouth of the Mersey, through Ellesmere Port (where barge canals branch off to the Potteries district of north Staffordshire), the oil depot of Stanlow, and the chemical and soap manufacturing towns of Runcorn and Warrington, to the terminal docks at Trafford Park. Manchester is now the fourth port of the United Kingdom, by value of its trade, the chief imports being wheat, fruit, raw cotton, petroleum, and timber.

II. The Middle Mersey Manufacturing Region

Around the head of the Mersey estuary is a group of towns —Widnes, Warrington, Runcorn, St Helens—which specialize in the manufacture of chemicals, soap, and glass.

One of the factors which led to the location of the chemical industry in this region is the proximity to the salt-field of

D

Cheshire, which provides the chief raw material for the manufacture of the 'heavy' chemicals. The salt is found in thick beds several hundred feet below the surface, but is not now obtained by mining. Instead, pairs of bore-holes are put down to the salt beds, fresh water is run down one

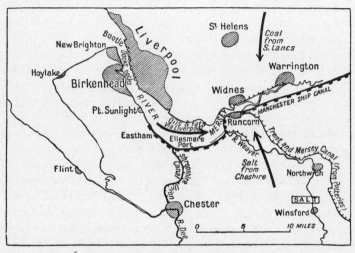

FIG. 36. THE MOUTHS OF THE MERSEY AND THE DEE
(Arrows show the sources of the chief products needed for the manufacture of chemicals, glass, and salt)

of them and brine pumped up the other. To obtain salt the brine is evaporated to dryness and the residue purified. Though nowadays chlorine and other chemicals are made on the salt-field by the use of electricity, formerly it was necessary to use large quantities of coal. Consequently the chemical industry grew up around the Mersey estuary, midway between the salt-field and the coal-field, and on a navigable waterway. The construction of barge canals to both the salt-field and the coal-field and the construction of the Manchester

Ship Canal for the import of other raw materials and the export of the finished products, gave to the mid-Mersey region the added advantage of cheap transport.

The chief centres of the industry are Widnes and Runcorn, though since the application of electrical processes Northwich on the Cheshire salt-field, and Fleetwood in north Lancashire, where salt is also obtained, have also become very important centres of the chemical industry.

Soap. The chief raw materials necessary for the manufacture of soap are fat or oil, caustic soda or caustic potash, and common salt. The fat used is mostly tallow obtained from the great sheep-rearing countries such as Argentina and Australia, and the oils are mostly such vegetable oils as palm-kernel oil, copra oil, and ground-nut oil, which are produced in Liverpool from raw materials imported from tropical countries. Caustic soda and caustic potash are products of the mid-Mersey chemical industry, and salt is of course easily obtainable from the Cheshire salt-field, while the large quantities of coal which are required by the soap factories can readily be obtained from the Lancashire coal-field. There is, indeed, hardly any district in the world where the materials necessary for the production of soap can so easily be assembled as on the Mersey estuary. Widnes and Warrington are the chief centres of the industry, but Port Sunlight, at the mouth of the Manchester Ship Canal, has the largest soap factory in the world, and there are also many factories in the Liverpool and Manchester districts.

Glass. The chief raw materials necessary for the manufacture of glass are pure sand, sodium carbonate, and limestone, which are fused together in a furnace generating a temperature of 1300° C. or 1500° C. Sand is imported via the Mersey and the Manchester Ship Canal, limestone is easily obtainable from Derbyshire, and the sodium carbonate and other chemicals used are produced in the locality, while coal is obtained from the Lancashire coal-field. The chief centre of the glass industry is St Helens.

Liverpool grew up on a sandstone ridge which formed the only way across the mosses or marshes which formerly occupied a large portion of southern Lancashire. At the point where this ridge approaches the coast a small inlet, called the Pool, provided an anchorage for ships, and it was there that the first small port arose. Until the fifteenth century, however, Liverpool was completely overshadowed by Chester, which was the chief port for Ireland; but, as ships became larger, and the estuary of the Dee silted up, Liverpool began to grow in importance. In the eighteenth century its prosperity was based largely on the famous, or infamous, 'triangular run.' Ships sailed from Liverpool to West Africa with cheap trinkets and spirits, with which they bought slaves; these were taken to the West Indies, where a cargo of sugar, tobacco, or cotton was loaded, for the homeward run eastward to Liverpool. Thus, at the beginning of the Industrial Revolution, Liverpool had already established trade relations with America, and inevitably became the centre for the importation of the raw cotton and the foodstuffs required by the rapidly increasing industrial population. In modern times finely equipped docks have been built along a thirty-mile frontage on the Liverpool side of the bottle-necked estuary, and similar, though less extensive facilities, have been provided at Birkenhead, on the Cheshire side.

The combined ports of Liverpool-Birkenhead are now second only to London in the value of their trade, while the facilities for the importation of raw materials have led to the rise of important manufacturing industries. The chief imports are cotton, meat, grain, flour, vegetable oils, hides and skins, and tobacco. The chief industries are flour-milling, the manufacture of soap, chemicals, tobacco, and cattle cake, engineering, and the building of motor-cars.

As an exporting centre it serves a vast hinterland embracing both northern England and the Midlands, the chief exports being manufactured goods, such as cottons, woollens, machinery, soap, and chemicals. As a passenger port it is still a close rival to Southampton, though it has suffered somewhat through its remoteness from London, and from the necessity of constant dredging to keep the channel deep enough for the very largest ocean liners.

Birkenhead, which is connected to Liverpool by ferry and tunnels, has shipbuilding yards and marine engineering shops. It imports meat from Australia and Argentina, and beef cattle from Ireland.

III. The Industrial Districts of the North-west (see p. 49)

The Cumberland, or Whitehaven, coal-field is one of the minor areas of coal production, its annual output being only 1 per cent of the country's total production. The coal-seams dip westward from the edge of the Cumbrian Mountains, and some of the workings extend for three or four miles under the sea. There is also a large concealed coal-field under the Solway Plain, but the seams are so deep that they will probably never be worked.

Iron ore is mined in three centres in the north-western district, viz.:

(1) At Cleator Moor and Egremont, a few miles south-east of Whitehaven.

(2) Near Millom, on the western shore of the Duddon estuary.

(3) At Dalton, in the Furness district of Lancashire.

More than three-quarters of the ore produced in the north-western area comes from the first-named district, Millom and

Dalton-in-Furness producing respectively 7 per cent and 15 per cent of the total.

The ore produced in all three districts is of excellent quality, and its iron content is very high. Unfortunately, it is difficult to mine because of:

(1) The irregular character of the deposits.

(2) The depth of the beds, which necessitates the ore being 'won' by mining, instead of by quarrying, which is the practice in other British iron-mining districts.

(3) The hardness of the ore, which prevents the use of 'steam-navvies,' such as are used in other districts.

Nearly all the ore mined is used locally, though small quantities are sent to Scotland and to Middlesbrough. Unfortunately, the Cumberland coal is not very suitable for use in the blast furnaces, so coke is 'imported' from Durham, Wigan, and Barnsley, while much of the local coal is 'exported' to Northern Ireland.

The chief smelting towns are Workington, Millom, and Barrow. The last-named town is also an important ship-building centre, and has great engineering shops, jute factories, and paper works.

Calder Hall, near Whitehaven, is the site of the first British 'reactor' for the generation of atomic energy.

RAILWAYS OF NORTHERN ENGLAND

Railway transport in northern England is shared by two systems—the former London Midland and Scottish and the former London and North Eastern. The one serves chiefly the western side and the other the eastern side, though the two systems interlock on the York, Derby, and Notts. coal-field, and are linked by several trans-Pennine lines.

On the Lancashire and Cheshire plain the main line from

London runs from Crewe northward through Warrington, Preston, and Lancaster, situated at the heads of the estuaries of the Mersey, the Ribble, and the Lune respectively.   Beyond

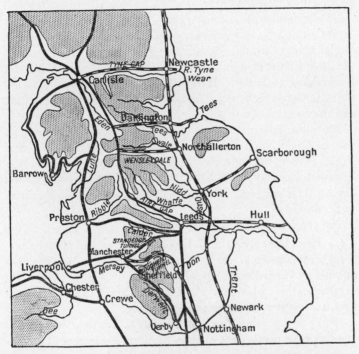

FIG. 37. DIAGRAM MAP OF RAILWAYS OF NORTHERN ENGLAND

Lancaster the line climbs over Shap Fell, which links the Cumbrian Mountains to the Pennines, and then runs via Penrith to Carlisle. Liverpool and Manchester are linked by main lines, and each city is the centre of routes radiating to the surrounding industrial districts. Fleetwood and Heysham, as packet stations from which fast passenger and mail steamers ply to the Isle of Man and Ireland, are served by express 'boat trains,' and a coastal route branching off at Carnforth serves the Furness iron and steel district and the Whitehaven coal-field.

On the eastern side of the Pennines the main 'Midland' line enters the district midway between Derby and Nottingham, but has loop lines through both cities. The line runs northward at the foot of the Pennines, through Chesterfield, Sheffield, and Rotherham, to Leeds. Here it turns northwestward through the Aire Gap, climbs the Pennines by the upper Ribble valley, and then runs down the Eden valley to Carlisle.

The main line of the former L.N.E.R. follows the route of the old Great North Road,[1] through Newark, Doncaster, and York, passes through the Northallerton Gap between the Pennines and the North York Moors, and then runs via Darlington, Durham, and Newcastle to Berwick-on-Tweed and so to Scotland.

The chief trans-Pennine routes are:

(1) From Derby via the valley of the Derwent to Manchester.

(2) From Sheffield via Penistone and the Woodhead tunnel (3 miles 13 yards long) to Manchester.

(3) From Huddersfield via the Standedge tunnel (3 miles 57 yards long) to Manchester.

(4) From Leeds via the Calder valley to Todmorden, whence one line runs north-westward to Burnley, Preston, and Blackpool, and another runs south-westward to Manchester.

(5) The main line from Leeds via the Aire Gap to Carlisle, with important branches to east Lancashire, Lancaster, and Barrow-in-Furness.

(6) From Northallerton via the valley of the Ure (Wensleydale) to Hawes Junction.

---

[1] The present Great North Road (Ministry of Transport Route A 1) goes through Wetherby, well to the west of York.

(7) From Darlington via the valleys of the Tees and the Greta into the Vale of Eden, and thence to Barrow. This route is the highest trans-Pennine line, but is of great importance for the transport of coke from Durham to the Furness district.

(8) From Newcastle to Carlisle via the Tyne Gap.

EXAMINATION QUESTIONS

1. Point out five natural routes across the Pennine Hills, and show what use is made of each.   (O. S. C.)

2. Describe the position of the most important centre in England for the manufacture (*a*) of cotton; (*b*) of woollen goods. Explain briefly why the industry settled in each centre. What are the chief sources of raw material in each case?   (C. S. C.)

3. Explain, as fully as you can, why raw cotton is an important import into Liverpool, and raw wool an important import into London.   (L. G. S.)

4. Describe the Pennines under the headings of (*a*) scenery; (*b*) uses to man. State briefly how these highlands have affected communications in *either* a north–south *or* an east–west direction.

(N. U.)

5. Three important rivers run over, or on the edge of, the Durham and Northumberland coal-field, giving rise to three important groups of towns. Explain this statement, and indicate the industrial characteristics of the three groups.   (L. M.)

6. Give the geographical factors that are favourable to the location of the major cotton and woollen industries of England on the two opposite sides of the Pennines.   (D. M.)

7. Write a geographical account of the chemical industries of the Mersey basin, explaining carefully why they are located there.

(D. M.)

8. With the aid of sketch-maps and diagrams, describe the major features of the relief and structure of *either* Northumberland *or* County Durham.   (D. M.)

* D

9. Describe carefully the relief and drainage of the Pennine Chain, indicating any important gaps in that upland. (L. G. S.)

10. Draw a large sketch-map of the coal-field of *either* Northumberland and Durham *or* south Lancashire, inserting *four* towns on the coal-field. Select *two* dissimilar industries of the region, describe where they are, and the factors contributing to their development.
(C. S. C.)

11. What is meant by the 'hinterland' of a port?   Illustrate your answer by reference to the trade of Liverpool and Hull.   (D. M.)

12. Draw a simple sketch-map of the Pennines, showing the distribution of the coal-fields. Name the coal-fields and mark the chief towns of each. What are the chief manufactures of the coal-fields? Has their contact with other countries played any part in this respect? (D. S. C.)

13. Contrast the textile trade of Lancashire with that of Yorkshire, and state what geographical factors have caused the trades to differ.   (C. S. C.)

14. Write a geographical account of the country drained by *either* the River Tyne *or* the Yorkshire Ouse, paying particular attention to the extent of the area, the relief and occupations.   (D. S. C.)

15. With the aid of a sketch-map or maps, give a reasoned account of the distribution of population in England north of the Trent (*approximately* north of the latitude of Derby).   (L. G. S.)

16. Show the part played by physical conditions and special resources on the development of textile industries on the opposite flanks of the Pennines.   (W. M.)

17. Draw a map to show in some detail the physical features of England, north of a line from Lincoln to Chester. Insert on it two fishing ports; two small country market towns; two large industrial centres; two health resorts; two large cities. Indicate important regions of production of any two of the following: rubber tyres, poultry, flour, cattle foods, soap.

Outline the reasons for the location of one town and one industry mentioned on your map.   (D. M.)

18. Summarize the physical geography of Yorkshire. Give one example of a market town, one of an industrial centre, and one port, and discuss the reasons for their development in relation to their physical surroundings in that county.   (D. M.)

19. Describe the surface features and climate of the English Lake District, and show how these influence the position of the towns and villages and the size of its population. (O. S. C.)

20. Describe the position of *three* ports on the east coast of Great Britain north of the Wash which trade extensively with north-western Europe, excluding the Baltic ports. Selecting *two* of them, give an account of their trade with the ports of north-western Europe. (C. S. C.)

CHAPTER VII

EASTERN ENGLAND

THIS region will be dealt with under the three headings of Lincolnshire, the Fenlands, and East Anglia.

I. LINCOLNSHIRE

From the point of view of position only, this county is part of northern England, but from the standpoints of structure, relief, climate, and occupations of the people, it undoubtedly belongs to the south-eastern part of the country. The dominant physical features of the county are the chalk and limestone scarps which are a continuation of those of south-eastern England, and which form the Lincoln Heights (Heath, or Edge) and the Lincoln Wolds. Between these two scarps is a broad clay vale; to the west of the Heights, and between them and the Trent, is a red clay vale; and between the Wolds and the sea is a belt of coastal marshes (see Fig. 38).

Farming. The chalk and limestone scarps nowhere rise much above the 500-foot line, and are, moreover, covered with a mantle of sand and clay laid down by the glaciers of the Ice Age. Consequently, arable farming can be carried on up to the summits of the hills, as well as on the plains. More-over, the region is situated on the drier, sunnier side of Britain, and the annual rainfall of twenty-five to thirty inches favours the growth of root crops and cereals. Lincoln-shire is, therefore, one of the chief farming counties of

Britain, and, because of its variety of relief and soil, has developed both arable and pastoral farming to a remarkable degree.

On the Wolds and the Heath the 'Norfolk' fourfold system of rotation is modified to produce crops of wheat and oats;

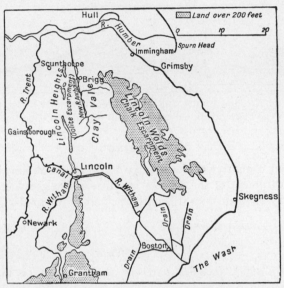

FIG. 38. LINCOLNSHIRE

turnips, potatoes, and sugar-beet; barley; and clover or peas. All are 'money' crops, except turnips and clover, and these are used as winter food for cattle and sheep. By this method far more sheep can be kept than on a similar area of permanent grassland, and so the upland areas of Lincolnshire are noteworthy for sheep-rearing.

Cattle are reared in all districts as part of the general farming system, but are most numerous in the central clay vale and on the coastal marshes, where young stock are fattened for sale to butchers.

Market gardening is carried on in the Fenland around Boston, and in the 'miniature Fenland' of the Isle of Axholme between the Rivers Trent, Don, and Idle.

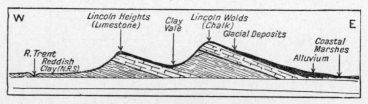

FIG. 39. SECTION ACROSS LINCOLNSHIRE
(The black streak indicates alluvial and glacial deposits)

IRON-MINING

About a quarter of the country's iron ore is obtained from the escarpment of the Lincoln Heights, and a great smelting industry has grown up at Scunthorpe and Frodingham.

II. THE FENLANDS

This district includes parts of the counties of Lincoln, Huntingdon, Cambridge, and Norfolk and is crossed by the Rivers Witham, Welland, Nen, and Great Ouse. Ages ago it was a broad shallow bay, which was gradually filled up with mud swept in by the tides and brought down by the rivers. In the marshes thus formed, sedges and other water-loving plants grew in abundance, and by their decay formed vast deposits of peat which vary in thickness from a few inches to fifteen feet. Even before Roman times portions of the silt lands near the Wash had been embanked and drained, but the peaty lands which lie farther from the sea remained

desolate marshes until the seventeenth century, when the
Dukes of Bedford reclaimed more than 150 square miles
of the tract now known as the Bedford Level. In the

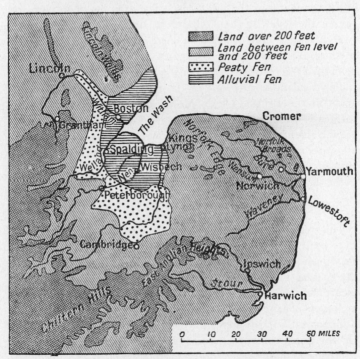

FIG. 40. THE FENLANDS AND EAST ANGLIA

following century further extensive schemes of reclamation
were carried out, and now there remain only one or two
small areas of original fen. The principal method of drainage
consists of the construction of canals which tap the waters
of the uplands before they reach the lowlands. The former
Fenland is crossed by many minor dykes from which the

water is pumped into the main canals, the outlet to the sea being through sluice-gates which are opened by the pressure of the dyke-water at low tide, and are closed by the pressure of the sea-water as the tide rises. The draining of the sub-soil causes the level of the Fenland to sink about a foot every twelve years. The consequent increase in the risk of flooding is being countered by the construction of new cut-off channels near the eastern side of the Fens and around Spalding.

The Fenland is now one of the most intensively cultivated areas in the British Isles. More than three-quarters of the surface is under plough, and wheat, potatoes, and sugar-beet are the chief farm crops. Fruit-growing and market gardening are important industries on the fertile alluvial soil around Boston, Wisbech, and Spalding, and the last-named town is noted as the centre of the British bulb-growing industry.

III. East Anglia

This region comprises the counties of Norfolk and Suffolk. It is built chiefly of chalk, which forms a low escarpment in the south-west, and an undulating plateau in the north. In the eastern half of the area the gentle dip slope of the chalk escarpment is covered with boulder clay, and on the coast are layers of sandy rocks containing many shells.

The coast has suffered many changes during historic times. On the north coast, to the east of Cromer, the cliffs are being cut back at a rate varying from 100 yards to 500 yards per century, and many villages have been entirely destroyed during the last few centuries. Much of the material derived from the wastage of the cliffs in this area is washed southward by the tidal currents and deposited on the east coast of Norfolk, forming sand-spits, which partially close up the mouths of the rivers, or divert them southward. Some of the shallow lakes known as the Norfolk Broads are remnants of a large lake which was cut off from the sea by a sand-spit and others occupy hollows left by peat-cutting in the Middle Ages.

Farming. It was in East Anglia that the modern farming method of rotating cereals with root crops and clover was first introduced to Britain, during the Agrarian Revolution of the eighteenth century. Arable farming is still the main-stay of the region, wheat being grown chiefly on the heavier, clayey soils, and barley on the lighter, sandy soils which receive very low rainfall. In modern times the granting of a subsidy has encouraged the farmers to substitute sugar-beet for turnips, and the district is now the chief area for the production of this crop.

Fruit-growing is important in Norfolk, which is specially noted for the production of strawberries, gooseberries, and black currants.

TOWNS AND MANUFACTURING INDUSTRIES OF EASTERN ENGLAND

Lincoln grew up on an easily defended height where the Roman road following the Lincoln Edge crossed the Witham Gap. The Witham itself was navigable to Lincoln, and the Foss Dyke, an artificial waterway connecting the Witham and the Trent, gave it 'back-door' entrance via the Humber. In modern times its command of the Witham Gap has made it the focus of roads and railways, and these in their turn have made it the market town for the surrounding agricultural district. Local deposits of iron ore, though not now worked, led to the development of an iron and steel industry, which formerly specialized in the manufacture of agricultural implements. Nowadays the industry draws its pig iron from Scunthorpe, and has, moreover, changed its character, the chief specialization being the manufacture of excavating mach-inery, of which Lincoln is the world's most important centre.

Scunthorpe, already mentioned as an iron-mining town, has also developed an important iron and steel industry which produces about one-seventh of the national output.

Grimsby and *Immingham* have already been dealt with as ports of the Humber (see p. 68).

In the Fenlands a double row of towns may be noted, viz.:

(*a*) Those situated at the inland limit of the Fens, and at the former head of boat navigation on the rivers. Such are Cambridge, Peterborough, and Stamford, situated on the Rivers Cam, Nen, and Welland respectively.

(*b*) More modern ports near the mouths of the rivers— Boston on the Witham, Spalding on the Welland, Wisbech on the Nen, and King's Lynn on the Great Ouse. Silting of the river mouths, and the increasing size of ships, have caused a great decline in the trade of all these ports, though *Boston* still imports some timber and exports coal, while *King's Lynn* imports fertilizer and cattle cake.

Norwich grew up round a castle built on high ground near the confluence of the Wensum and the Yare. It is an agricultural market town and manufactures mustard, starch, boots and shoes, agricultural implements, and traction engines.

Yarmouth and *Lowestoft* are twin ports, the former being situated at the mouth of the combined Waveney and Yare, and the latter on Lowestoft Ness, an accumulation of shingle which diverted the Waveney northward. Both are fishing ports engaged primarily in the herring industry, but Yarmouth has a small amount of general trade.

Ipswich is situated on the Orwell, at the lowest bridge-point, at the tidal limit, and at the head of navigation. It was an important port in the Middle Ages, but has suffered the same fate as other river ports.

Harwich is a packet station at the seaward end of a peninsula which juts into the combined estuary of the Orwell and the Stour. It is well served by express boat trains from London, the Midlands, and the north, and by fast packet steamers which ply to Holland and Belgium. A train ferry which can carry whole trains plies between Harwich and Zeebrugge in Belgium.

EXAMINATION QUESTIONS

1. Compare, and contrast, Lancashire with Norfolk in regard to human activities. Explain the *contrasts* that you mention. (L. M.)

2. For two districts of nearly the same area, *A* in east England, *B* in north-west England, the following statistics are given:

	A (acres)	*B* (acres)
Corn crops . . .	341,582 (36·1%)	72,116 (7·5%)
Root and grass crops .	192,328 (20·5%)	133,439 (13·9%)
Permanent pasture .	182,107 (19·2%)	366,038 (38·0%)
Wood and uncultivated .	227,460 (24·2%)	389,460 (40·6%)

(*a*) Draw two diagrams to the same scale to bring out the contrasts between the two districts.

(*b*) Discuss the probable reasons for the differences observed.

(C. S. C.)

3. Name the chief wheat-growing districts in England and state the conditions under which wheat is successfully grown in this country. Explain why wheat is not so extensively cultivated in Ireland or in Scotland. (C. S. C.)

CHAPTER VIII

THE MIDLAND TRIANGLE

THIS region is situated within the triangular framework formed by the southern edge of the Pennines, the eastern edge of the Welsh mountains, and the oolite scarp of the Cotswolds and the Northampton Uplands. Within this triangle of high land is a triangle of rivers: the Severn on the west, the Trent on the north, and the Avon and the Soar, tributaries of the Severn and the Trent respectively, on the south-east and east.

The rocks which compose the region also fall into three groups, viz.:

(1) The *New Red Sandstone*, which comprises both reddish sandstone and reddish clay. These rocks were formed millions of years ago when the region was a great desert comparable to the Sahara, the sandstone being composed of wind-blown grains, and the clay being the mud which was deposited in salt lakes. As the clay is easily worn away by the weather, it forms nearly level plains, while the sandstone, which is slightly more resistant, forms low plateaus.

(2) *'Islands' of hard, old rock*, such as granite and slate. The largest of these hill masses are:

(*a*) Charnwood Forest, a region of craggy hills and deep valleys rising up suddenly from the surrounding plain of reddish clay. The 'forest' is a 'playground' for the neighbouring towns of Leicester and Loughborough.

(*b*) The Lickey Hills, south of Birmingham, where is

situated the famous Lickey Incline, the steepest slope on any British main line of railway.

(c) The Wrekin, an isolated hill mass rising abruptly from the Shropshire plain.

(3) The *coal-measures*, which also form 'islands' rising

FIG. 41. MIDLANDS—PHYSICAL AND GEOLOGICAL SKETCH-MAPS

above the general level of the clay plain. On the northern edge of the 'triangle' are:

(a) the southern end of the Yorks, Derby, and Notts. coal-field; and

(b) the north Staffordshire coal-field.

In the centre of the triangle are:

(c) the Leicestershire coal-field;

(d) the Warwickshire coal-field; and

(e) the south Staffordshire coal-field.

On the borders of Wales are the Severn valley coal-fields:

(f) Coalbrookdale; and

(g) the Forest of Wyre.

Occupations of the People

The human activities of the Midland Triangle may also be considered under three headings, viz.: farming, mining, and manufacturing.

I. FARMING

As the region lies beteeen the wetter west and the drier east, the farming activities are fairly representative of those of the whole country.

Cattle-rearing, for both meat and milk, is of predominant importance, and most of the Midland counties have more than three-quarters of the cultivated land under permanent grass. The district around Melton Mowbray, in Leicestershire, is specially noted for the fattening of beef cattle. As the animals are sold on the approach of winter, the farmers have ample leisure, and so this area has become the chief fox-hunting district in Britain. Melton Mowbray is also noted for the manufacture of Stilton cheese, named after a village in Huntingdonshire where it was marketed.

Sheep-rearing is carried on chiefly on the limestone scarp which forms the south-eastern boundary of the region, and on pasture and arable in the eastern half of Leicestershire.

Fruit-growing is the dominant industry in the Vale of Evesham, which is drained by the Warwickshire Avon. Conditions favouring the development of the fruit industry in this area are: the minor 'Gulf of Winter Warmth' which extends up the Bristol Channel and the lower Severn valley; the light, porous soil which is underlaid by a water-bearing layer; and the local practice of land tenure, which favours the establishment of smallholdings.

II. MINING

Coal. Excluding the southern end of the Yorks, Derby, and Notts. coal-field, the Midland coal-fields produce only 6 per cent of the coal of Britain. Of this percentage the north Staffordshire coal-field accounts for considerably more than one-third, the Warwickshire coal-field for nearly one-third, and the Leicestershire coal-field for one-fifth; south Staffordshire, in spite of the large area of its coal-field as shown on the maps, is now of very minor importance as a coal-mining area.

Iron. The limestone scarps which form the south-eastern edge of the Midland Triangle supply more than half of the British iron ore, the chief mining (or quarrying) areas being around Northampton, Kettering, and Corby. The last-named town is now one of our chief iron- and steel-producing centres.

Gypsum, a white, fibrous mineral found in thin seams in the New Red Sandstone rocks, is obtained from shallow workings and quarries in Nottinghamshire and Derbyshire. It is used in the pottery industry, and is ground up to make plaster of Paris.

Granite and similar hard rocks for use as road metal and paving-stones are quarried in Charnwood Forest and the neighbouring hill mass of Mount Sorrel.

III. MANUFACTURING

(a) *The Metal Industries*

The processes which revolutionized the iron and steel industries during the eighteenth century were first introduced on the small coal-fields of the Welsh borders, and for a time this region was the chief centre of the iron industry.

Ironbridge, on the Severn, received its name from the fact that the first iron bridge was built there. Local supplies of coal and iron were scanty, however, and the industry soon shifted to south Staffordshire, where metal-working had long been carried on, and where there were abundant supplies of both

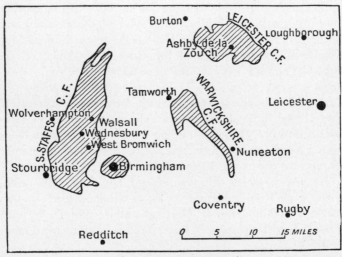

FIG. 42. SOUTH STAFFORDSHIRE, WARWICKSHIRE, AND LEICESTER-SHIRE COAL-FIELDS

coal and iron. The Black Country, as the mining and manufacturing area of south Staffordshire is still called, soon became 'one great workshop both above ground and below.' At night it was lurid with the flames of iron furnaces, and by day it seemed 'one vast, loosely knit town of humble homes, cinder heaps, and fields stripped of vegetation by smoke and fumes.' [1]

Nowadays very little smelting is done in the region, so the

[1] Mackinder, *Britain and the British Seas.*

term Black Country is hardly appropriate. It is, however, still the home of a very varied metal industry, and specializes in the manufacture of articles which are valuable in proportion to their bulk and to the amount of raw material needed in their manufacture. The reasons for such specialization are:

(1) The distance from the sea, and from sources of raw materials. This makes it difficult for the district to compete with other more favourably situated areas in the manufacture of bulky articles. Transport, however, adds little to the cost of small articles which take little raw material but depend for their value chiefly on the skill and labour necessary for their manufacture, and so the Black Country is at no disadvantage in the manufacture of such articles.

(2) The former lack of good roads within the area itself. Before the Industrial Revolution all transport in the area was by pack-horse, and so the inhabitants found it necessary to specialize in such small metal goods as buttons and buckles. The existence of a reservoir of skilled labour, used to the manufacture of small and comparatively intricate articles, helped to determine the modern specialization of the district.

Birmingham, though not strictly speaking in the Black Country, not on the coal-field, and not even in Staffordshire, is the metropolis of the region. Its manufactures are characterized by their great variety, some of the chief being: articles made of brass, copper, enamel, and aluminium; electro-plate, wireless apparatus, and jewellery.

Wolverhampton, sometimes called the 'capital of the Black Country,' shares in the hardware industry, and specializes in the making of tinware, locks and keys, and electrical plant. Other towns in the Black Country are noted for specialized branches of the metal industry which probably owe their origin to local inventions, or to the chance selection of a particular district for the manufacture of a special product. West Bromwich, for example, is noted for the manufacture of springs and weigh scales, Wednesbury for heavy iron and steel goods, and Walsall, which was formerly noted for the manufacture of saddlery and harness, now specializes in the interior fittings for motor-cars.

(b) The Motor Industry

Birmingham and various Black Country towns have for centuries specialized in the manufacture of wheeled vehicles, so it was natural that the district should become the home of the motor industry. Birmingham is noted for the manufacture of the Morris commercial cars, and Wolverhampton for the manufacture of motor-cycles. Coventry, situated nearly twenty miles south-east of Birmingham, and drawing its supplies of coal from the Warwickshire coal-field, was noted for the manufacture of ribbons in the eighteenth century, for bicycles in the nineteenth, and is now one of the chief centres for the manufacture of motor-cars.

(c) The Pottery Industry

The chief pottery-making centre in Britain, and indeed in the whole world, is Stoke-on-Trent, which is situated near the centre of the north Staffordshire coal-field. This district, which is often called the Potteries, contains more than three-quarters of the pottery workers of Britain. Yet it is difficult to assess the geographical factors which have caused this remarkable development of the industry. There is, it is true, plenty of coal for firing the furnaces, and plenty of local clay which is suitable for making coarse earthenware. But other coal-fields also produce these indispensable raw materials, and have almost equal facilities for the development of a pottery industry. One of the chief reasons why the industry grew up in north Staffordshire rather than elsewhere is that Josiah Wedgwood, 'the father of English pottery,' established his factories there in the middle of the eighteenth century.

The local clay is still used for the manufacture of drain-pipes, tiles, and other coarse earthenware, as well as for the 'saggars,' or containers in which the finer pottery is placed for firing in the kilns; but all the raw material for the manufacture of the true pottery and porcelain have to be brought from other districts. Of these raw materials the chief are: china clay, or kaolin, which comes from Cornwall; flint from the Channel coast of France; special ball clay from Dorset; and bone from Argentina and other ranching countries. Most of these materials are imported via the Mersey, and then sent to the Potteries by the Trent and Mersey Canal.

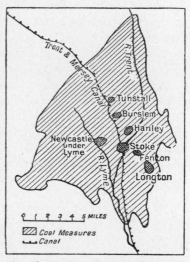

FIG. 43. THE NORTH STAFFORDSHIRE OR POTTERIES COAL-FIELD

The Potteries is sometimes called 'the district of the five towns,' but there were originally six pottery towns—Tunstall, Burslem, Hanley, Stoke, Fenton, and Longton—strung along a six-mile strip, and these were amalgamated to form the County Borough (now the City) of Stoke-on-Trent.

The appearance of the pottery towns is very different from that of other industrial towns of Britain. Though there is much smoke, there are fewer factory chimneys than in Lanca-shire or Yorkshire towns; instead, there is 'a fantastic collec-tion of narrow-necked jars or bottles peeping above the house-tops on every side, looking as if gigantic biblical characters, after a search for oil or wine, had popped them there, among the dwarf streets. These, of course, are the pottery kilns and ovens, which are usually tall enough to be seen above the rows of cottage houses.' (J. B. Priestley, *English Journey*.)

These 'beehive,' coal-fired ovens are, however, now being extensively replaced by gas-fired tunnel kilns, which often run for years without interruption.

Within the district there is some degree of specialization. Tunstall, Burslem, and Hanley at the northern end are engaged principally in the manufacture of earthenware, while Stoke, in the centre, manufactures the highest class of china, and Longton and Fenton, at the southern end, make cheaper qualities.

(d) The Manufacture of Boots and Shoes

The leather industry naturally arose in the market towns which served the cattle- and sheep-rearing districts, and although most of the hides and skins are now imported, the industry is still centred in some of these towns. In the Midlands, Stafford, Leicester, Northampton, and Kettering are important centres for the manufacture of boots and shoes.

The Canal System of the Midlands

During the last decade of the eighteenth century, and before the first modern hard-surfaced roads were built, there was a great boom in canal construction. Birmingham, situ-ated near the centre of the country, and already the centre of a rapidly expanding industrial area, was the natural focus for the canals of the Midlands, and was soon linked to the four great estuaries—the Mersey, the Humber, the Severn, and the Thames—which are roughly equidistant from it. For some years these canals were of the greatest value to the expanding industries, but unfortunately they were of varying width and depth, and could accommodate only small boats. Consequently, with the advent of railways, traffic on the canals rapidly declined, and many of them became derelict, though a few, such as the Aire and Calder Navigation and canalized river Trent, are still of great importance for the transport of coal, grain, oil, and other bulky products, while the Grand Union Canal now provides through transport by hundred-ton motor-drawn barges between the London docks and Birmingham, and the Berkeley Canal links Gloucester with the Severn Estuary.

EXAMINATION QUESTIONS

1. Show on a sketch-map the approximate limits of the midlands of England; also the position and relation to river valleys of *one* important centre for each of the following industries: brewing, boot-making, hosiery, bicycles. Suggest reasons why the industries have settled round each centre. (C. S. C.)

2. Account for the great density of population of the area which may be said to have Birmingham as its commercial centre. (L. M.)

3. From the south-east of Lincolnshire into Warwickshire at least four 'natural regions' may be distinguished. Discuss this statement, and indicate any results which may be expected on production.

(L. G. S.)

4. Select and locate any *one* great iron and steel centre in the British Isles. Indicate how far the locality of your choice is self-supporting

or dependent on external sources in the matter of raw materials necessary for the development of the industry. (L. M.)

5. Name and locate four important coal-fields of Great Britain. What industries are connected with each? (L. M.)

6. Show by a sketch-map the traffic routes by which the manufactures of the Black Country reach the following ports: Liverpool, Grimsby, London, Bristol. (L. M.)

7. Describe the position of the Black Country and of the Potteries in relation to the basin of the Trent and to routes connecting these districts with Liverpool and with Bristol.

Mention some of the important centres of each district and give examples of their chief industries. (C. S. C.)

CHAPTER IX

THE SEVERN AND THE BRISTOL AVON

THE SEVERN BASIN

THE Severn, which is the longest river in Great Britain, rises in the mountain of Plynlimon, not more than fifteen miles from the shores of Cardigan Bay, and takes a semicircular

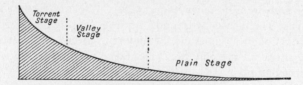

Profile section of a normal river

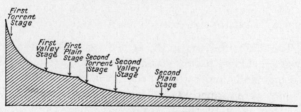

Diagrammatic profile section of the Severn

FIG. 44. RIVER PROFILES

course to the Bristol Channel. It is a composite river, formed probably by the union of three originally separate streams. The upper Severn, above Shrewsbury, was originally a tributary of the Dee, but was diverted to the south-east by the deposition of moraine during the Ice Age; the middle Severn is possibly the descendant of a stream which once flowed south-eastward to the Thames; and the lower Severn represents a stream which, working in the soft New Red Sandstone, cut back its head so rapidly that it 'captured' the middle Severn. This strange history accounts for the chief peculiarity of the Severn. Whereas most rivers have a gradually decreasing slope from the source to the sea (see the normal profile in Fig. 44), and are easily divisible into torrent stage, valley stage, and plain stage, the Severn has a profile like that of two rivers joined together. Before it reaches Shrewsbury it has already entered on its first plain stage, as can be seen from its meandering course. Beyond Shrewsbury it turns south-eastward, and, flowing through the gorge between Coalbrookdale and Bridgnorth, enters on its second valley stage. Emerging from this stage at Stourport, it enters on its second plain stage, which continues to the sea.

PHYSICAL DIVISIONS OF THE SEVERN BASIN (see Fig. 45)

(1) The *Vale of Powis* is the fertile lowland of the Welsh valley stage. Here pastoral farming predominates, with sheep on the highlands and cattle on the lowlands. Newtown and Welshpool were formerly noted for the manufacture of Welsh flannel, but most of the factories have had to close down in face of the competition of the West Riding and other well-equipped woollen-manufacturing districts.

(2) The *Shropshire Plain* is devoted to dairy farming in the north, where the land is clayey, and to arable farming in the south, where the soil is light and easily worked. *Shrewsbury*, situated within a loop of the river, first rose to importance as a fortress town, and is now the route centre and market town of the region. Near by is a small coal-field which supplies local needs.

(3) The *South Shropshire Hills*, which include the isolated mass of the Wrekin on the left bank, and Wenlock Edge and the Clee Hills on the right bank, are famed for their bold contours, beautiful scenery, and old-world villages.

(4) The *Severn Gorge* cuts through the two small coal-fields of Coalbrookdale and the Forest of Wyre. Though these fields are now of little importance they were at the beginning of the Industrial Revolution the chief manufacturing district in the country (see p. 103).

(5) The *Plain of Hereford* is a great hollow floored

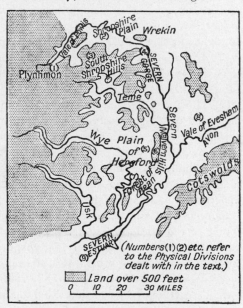

FIG. 45. THE SEVERN BASIN

with fertile Old Red Sandstone. Lying in the rain-shadow of the Welsh mountains it has a rather dry climate, and has, therefore, a considerable area under plough. It has many hop-fields and apple orchards and is also a notable cattle-rearing region.

(6) The *Malvern Hills*, which lie between the Severn and the Plain of Hereford, may be compared with Charnwood Forest (see page 100), since both consist of hard, old rocks thrust through the newer rocks of the plain.

E

(7) The *Forest of Dean*, which lies between the Rivers Wye and Severn, contains one of the minor coal-fields of Britain. By an ancient law any native of the district who has worked in a coal-mine for a year and a day has the right to dig for coal in any district not already being worked, and a few small pits are, in fact, owned by the miners themselves. The best seams are, however, nearing exhaustion, and the output is very small.

(8) The *Plain of Worcestershire* and the *Vale of Evesham* have already been dealt with in the chapter on the Midland Triangle (see page 102).

(9) The *Severn Estuary* is remarkable for its bore—a specially high tide which, at certain seasons, rushes up the river as a wall of water, causing a rise of as much as sixty feet at Chepstow. The bore, like the eger of the Trent and the phenomenally high tides of the Bay of Fundy in Canada, is caused by the oncoming wave of the tide being pent in between the gradually narrowing shores.

Gloucester, at the head of the Severn estuary, and at one corner of the Midland Triangle, seems to have great advantages as a port. Unfortunately, the channel is shallow, and the bore, instead of being a help, is a hindrance to navigation, so that Gloucester is accessible by only small steamers, despite the construction of a small ship canal to Sharpness. In recent years Gloucester has developed a great aircraft industry.

The Bristol Avon

The Bristol Avon rises on the dip slope of the Cotswolds, and for the first part of its course flows eastwards as if it were going to join the Thames below Malmesbury. Instead, it turns southward and then westward, and breaks through the Cotswold ridge in a fine gorge at Bath. After flowing through Bristol it cuts through a ridge of carboniferous limestone by a second gorge at Clifton.

The basin of the upper Avon in Wiltshire and the neighbouring parts of Gloucester and Somerset is often called the West of England District.   Before the Industrial Revolution

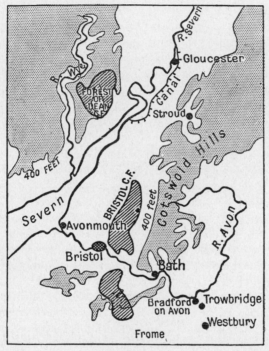

FIG. 46. THE SEVERN ESTUARY AND THE BRISTOL AVON

this was, as we have already seen (page 57), the chief centre for the manufacture of the fine, felted woollen cloth known as 'broadcloth.'   Factors which favoured the development of the industry in this area were:

(1) Local supplies of wool, from the sheep of the Cotswolds.

(It should be noted, however, that the local wool was not used for the manufacture of the best broadcloth.)

(2) Soft water from a bed of sandstone in the Cotswolds.

(3) Local supplies of fuller's earth for washing the wool.

(4) Water-power from the streams which flowed down the steep scarp slope of the Cotswolds.

With the advent of the Industrial Revolution the woollen industry of the west of England inevitably declined, but certain centres are still noted for special products: Stroud in Gloucestershire and Trowbridge in Wiltshire still manufacture suitings of high quality, as well as cloths for billiard tables and for tennis-ball coverings; Witney, in Oxfordshire, manufactures blankets; Wilton, which has given its name to carpets, now manufactures felt.

Bath owes its name and origin to the existence of warm mineral springs. It was a favourite residential centre in Roman times, and the restored Roman bath is one of the finest in the world. In the eighteenth century it again became a fashionable watering-place, and is to-day a popular residential centre.

Bristol, situated at the landward end of the Clifton Gorge, is the chief city of the region and one of the great ports of Britain. It first rose to importance as the port at which Irish produce was landed for conveyance overland to London, and in later times controlled a large share of the trade between Britain and America. As ships increased in size, however, its trade declined, and in spite of the construction of new docks in the early part of the nineteenth century, it has never regained its former importance. Well-equipped docks, capable of accommodating large ocean liners, have, however, been built at the outport of *Avonmouth*, which specializes in the importation of tobacco, petroleum, frozen meat, dairy produce, and bananas. Concentrated zinc ore, imported chiefly from Australia, is refined at Avonmouth in quantities sufficient to supply Britain's requirements of the metal.

The older industries of Bristol—the manufacture of cocoa, tobacco, and soap—owe their origin to the early importance of its trade with America. In modern times Bristol has become one of our chief centres of the aircraft industry.

The *Bristol coal-field* lies chiefly to the south of Bristol and entirely to the west of the Cotswolds. The coal is of poor quality, and the output is insufficient to supply the needs of Bristol and the surrounding district.

EXAMINATION QUESTIONS

1. What are the typical parts of a river's course, and in what respects do they differ from one another? Illustrate your answer by describing the course, from source to mouth, of *either* the Rhone *or* the Severn. (C. S. C.)

2. Choosing *either* the Severn *or* the Trent, describe the position within the *basin* of the river:

(*a*) of the parts suitable for agriculture;

(*b*) of the chief industrial centres, mentioning the distinctive industries of each centre. (C. S. C.)

CHAPTER X

WALES

The boundary between Wales and England follows fairly closely the edge of the high land, and this in its turn coincides approximately with the line dividing the hard, old rocks of the west from the softer, newer rocks of the English Midlands (see Fig. 7). Thus, when Nature built Britain, she marked out Wales as a region separate from England, in which man was likely to develop along different lines. During the Anglo-Saxon invasions, and for many centuries later, the mountains enabled the small, dark people whom we speak of as the Britons to retain their independence and to continue their own mode of life. Eventually, however, the mountains proved a source of weakness, for communication within the Principality was so difficult that centralized government and united effort were difficult to achieve, and the Welsh were gradually subdued by the English armies which penetrated by lowland routes into the heart of the country. The people, however, still retain many of their ancient customs, traditions, and characteristics, and except in the lowlands, where there have been large influxes of English, the Welsh tongue is still in common use, though all children also learn English in the schools.

Physical Divisions

In South Wales the structure lines run from west to east, as is shown by the grain of the highland and by the numerous rias which indent the south-western peninsula of Pembroke.

The highest mountains of this region are the Brecknock Beacons, which rise to a height of 2,910 feet. In the east the rivers—the Usk, the Taff, and the Neath—flow across

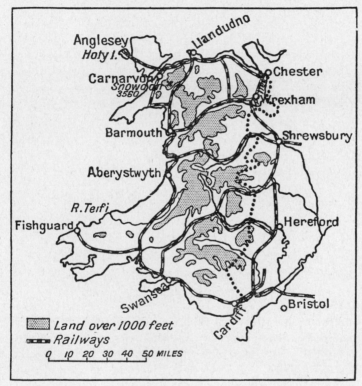

FIG. 47. WALES—RELIEF AND RAILWAYS

the grain of the land from north to south. In the west, however, the rivers—e.g. the Towy and Teifi—follow the grain of the land, their upper courses trending from northeast to south-west and their lower courses from east to west.

In central and northern Wales the structure lines run from north-east to south-west, and certain lines of weakness are followed by valleys which divide the high land into the following sub-regions.

(*a*) Anglesey and the northern coastal plain. Anglesey, though a lowland, is composed of hard, old rocks which have been worn down almost to sea-level. The Menai Straits are a rift valley which has sunk below the level of the sea.

(*b*) The Snowdon Range in Carnarvonshire, and the Arenig Range in Merioneth.

(*c*) The Berwyn Range, which is separated from the last-named highland by the trough in which lie the upper Dee, Lake Bala, and the River Mawddach. Lake Vyrnwy is really a reservoir constructed to supply Liverpool with water.

(*d*) Central Wales, which lies between the upper Severn and the Usk. In this region the mountains do not rise to such great heights as they do farther north, and there are several valleys which provide routes through the highland.

THE SOUTH WALES COAL-FIELD

Structurally, this coal-field may be likened to a badly shaped pie, the 'pie-dish' being the older rocks which crop out round the edges, and the 'pie-crust' being the coal-measures which sag downward from the rim but rise up again in the middle. The crust is, moreover, deeply scored by many valleys which cross the coal-field from north to south. These structural features have had far-reaching effects on the coal-mining industry and on the social life of the region. Mining first began on the northern edge of the coal-field where the seams are near the surface and could be worked in quarries. Later the seams began to be mined in the deep, steep-sided valleys; and at the present time most of the pits are situated near the middle of the coal-field, where the central roll of the strata brings them near the surface, and where the deep valleys enable the coal to be reached by comparatively shallow shafts. Population is, therefore, concentrated in the valleys, the intervening hills being practically unpeopled. The valleys are so narrow that there is room only for the road, the railway, and at most a few rows of houses; and there has, consequently, been no opportunity for the growth of even moderately sized towns, except in the few places where deep tributary valleys enter from east or west.

The existence of such a dense population in a district so unfavourable in many ways to the growth of human settlements is due largely to the fact that the coal is of exceptionally good quality. On the eastern and southern edge of the coal-field the coal is mostly of the ordinary household variety which contains a good deal of the volatile substances which cause it to flame and smoke when burnt. Such coal is said to be *bituminous*. Farther west is found the famous Welsh *steam coal*, which contains little volatile matter, and so burns with little flame or smoke, though it gives out great heat. Such coal is specially valuable for steamships, since a given quantity will drive a ship farther than the bituminous coals. The demand for bunker coal has, however, been greatly reduced by the increased use of oil fuel.

In the extreme west of the basin the coal is mainly *anthracite*, a variety which is practically pure carbon, contains little volatile matter, and so burns without flame or smoke or ash. It is largely used in the malting and cement-making industries and as smokeless fuel in specially constructed domestic stoves.

* E

Fig. 48 shows the general distribution of the above-mentioned types of coal in South Wales, but it should be noted that the change from one type to another is gradual, and that each type is not confined to the areas shown on the map.

THE IRON AND STEEL INDUSTRIES

Iron, like coal, was first mined on the northern edge of the coal-field, and so the iron and steel industries grew up there,

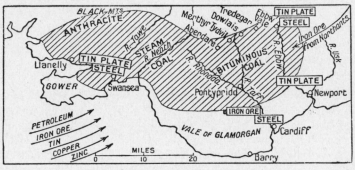

FIG. 48. SOUTH WALES COAL-FIELD

in such towns as Merthyr Tydfil, Dowlais, and Ebbw Vale. Before the end of last century, however, the local ore ceased to be mined as it was unsuitable for the new smelting processes, and although a small amount of high-quality ore is now mined on the southern edge of the coal-field nearly all the supplies are imported from North-West Africa, Sierra Leone, Spain, etc.

For a long time industrial inertia maintained the metal industries on the northern edge of the coal-field, but there was eventually a migration to the coast, and, although a modern steel and tin-plate factory has been erected at Ebbw Vale, the industry is chiefly concentrated near the ports.

Tin-plate, which consists of thin sheets of steel coated with a thin film of tin, is the chief speciality of South Wales. In the process of manufacture bars of steel are heated and pressed between rollers until they are reduced to the required thickness. In the older mills the sheets so formed were coated with tin by dipping in successive baths of sulphuric acid, palm-oil, and molten tin, but in the modern works the film of tin is deposited electrolytically.

Originally, the tin was brought from Cornwall, and the proximity to this supply of raw material possibly accounts for the rise of the industry in South Wales. Nowadays, however, little tin is produced in Cornwall, most of the world's supply coming from Bolivia, the Malay States, and Nigeria.

The chief centres for the manufacture of steel and tin-plate are Port Talbot, Llanelly, Swansea, and Cardiff. At Margam, near Port Talbot, is one of the world's largest steel mills, which makes steel for tin-plate in one continuous process from the arrival of the ore by ship at Port Talbot to the emergence of steel strip from the rolling mill five miles away along the coast.

Other industries of South Wales are the manufacture of 'galvanized' iron (the zinc-covered plate which is most familiar to us in the form of corrugated sheets for roofing), the smelting of copper and nickel, and the refining of petroleum.

The Coastal Plain

The Vale of Glamorgan, between the coal-field and the sea, is a fertile, mixed-farming area, which forms a marked contrast to the grim valleys of the mining area, and to the barren sheep moors of the Brecknock Beacons to the north of the coal-field.

The coastal plain has always been an important avenue of communication between southern England and Ireland. In order to safeguard this route the Normans built castles near the lowest crossing-places of the rivers, and the modern towns of Cardiff, Newport, etc., have grown up around these castles. Where, as in the cases of Newport, Cardiff, and Swansea, the ancient towns had also the advantages of easy access to coal, and of good harbours suitable for large vessels, the growth in modern times has been very rapid.

Newport is situated at the mouth of the Usk, and though not itself on the coal-field, is the focus of several mining valleys and has, therefore, a considerable export of coal. It also shares in the steel and tin-plate industries.

Cardiff is situated at the mouth of the Taff, and is an even more important focus of mining valleys than Newport. It is, therefore, the chief manufacturing centre of the region, and is such a convenient depot for the distribution of foodstuffs and of the raw materials required by the metal industries that it ranks as one of the greater ports of Britain. The city is now recognized as the capital of Wales.

Penarth and *Barry* are ports which are concerned chiefly with the export of coal.

Swansea is situated at the focus of the valleys which dissect the western end of the coal-field, and is noted for the manufacture of tin-plate, the smelting of copper and nickel, and the refining of oil, as well as for the bunkering of ships. *Port Talbot, Neath,* and *Llanelly* are other metal-working centres.

Milford Haven lies on a fine ria harbour, but its distance from the mining area has prevented its development as a commercial port or industrial centre. It is however now being developed as a great oil port capable of accommodating tankers up to 100,000 tons.

Pembroke, on the southern side of Milford Haven, is a minor naval station.

Fishguard is the terminus of the former Great Western Railway, and the packet station from which mail steamers ply to Rosslare in south-eastern Ireland.

Will F. Taylor

THE MENAI STRAITS

E. O. Hoppé

SYCHNANT PASS, NORTH WALES

CENTRAL WALES

This region is one of the most thinly peopled parts of the British Isles. It has no minerals and no large areas of lowland which could support a dense farming population. Sheep-rearing is the chief occupation of the people, and many of the formerly fertile valleys have been so neglected that they are now suitable only for sheep pastures. The almost extinct woollen industry of the upper Seven valley has already been mentioned (see page 112).

Aberystwyth, situated, as its name implies, at the mouth of the River Ystwyth, is a popular seaside resort and a university town.

Lake Vyrnwy and the Elan valley reservoirs supply water to Liverpool and Birmingham respectively.

NORTH WALES

This region, though not nearly so densely peopled as South Wales, has varied economic resources. In the east, near the English border, is the small coal-field of Flint and Denbigh, which supports the sheet-iron industry of Deeside and the miscellaneous industries of Wrexham, which is the chief town of the coal-field. Farther west, 'granite' is quarried for road metal near Conway and at other places on the coast. Slate is quarried at Nantlle, Bethesda, Llanberis, and Festiniog, which together produce nearly half the slate used in the British Isles. The high mountains, heavy rainfall, and numerous lakes suitable for storage reservoirs, make the Snowdon Range one of the most suitable districts in the British Isles for the generation of hydro-electricity. The largest generating stations are at Maentwrog and in the Conway valley.

The tourist industry is one of the chief sources of income

for the people. North Wales has the advantages of beautiful scenery, mild climate, and excellent railway services to London, the Midlands, and the industrial north. Along the

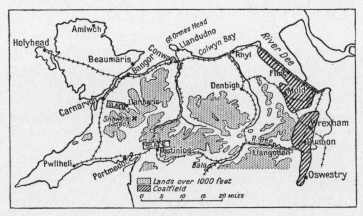

FIG. 49. NORTH WALES

north coast, where the mountains come close to the sea, is a string of holiday towns, of which the chief are Rhyl, Colwyn Bay, and Llandudno.

EXAMINATION QUESTIONS

1. (*a*) Compare the industrial areas of South Wales and north-east England (Northumberland, Durham, and north-east Yorks) from the standpoints of (i) mineral resources; (ii) facilities for export; (iii) economic activities. (*b*) On sketch-maps (i) name the chief rivers; (ii) mark the coal-fields; (iii) mark and name *three* large towns. (N. M.) (Outlines were given.)

2. Compare and contrast southern Lancashire and South Wales as regions in which a cotton industry might be developed. (L. G. S.)

3. What are the salient points in the relief and drainage of North

Wales? Point out the effects on the distribution of population and on the chief lines of communication. (L. M.)

4. Describe and explain the distribution of annual rainfall in Wales and the Welsh Marches, showing clearly the importance of position and relief in relation to climatic factors. (D. M.)

5. Name, in Great Britain, *one* area important for the manufacture of steel, and *one* for that of tin-plate. Describe the advantages of each area for its industry.

What raw materials are required and whence are they obtained?
(C. S. C.)

6. Describe the structure and relief of the South Wales coal-field and show how they have influenced (*a*) mining, and (*b*) the growth of inland and coastal towns. (D. M.)

7. Compare the mining and quarrying industries of North and South Wales. (W. M.)

8. Enumerate the occupations of the people of Wales, other than coal-mining. Show clearly how geographical conditions affect the occupations you name. (D. S. C.)

9. Compare the economic activities of the South Wales coal-field with those of *one* English coal-field. (W. M.)

10. Compare the overseas trade and the industries of Liverpool with those of Cardiff, making special reference to the influence upon the trade and industries of the hinterlands of the respective ports.
(L. M.)

11. Give an account of the features of the South Wales coal-field under the headings of: (*a*) position and extent; (*b*) major industries; (*c*) trade. Illustrate your answer with a sketch-map. (D. S. C.)

12. Draw a sketch-map of Wales and show on it those features and resources which have a definite influence on the distribution of population.

CHAPTER XI

THE SOUTH-WESTERN PENINSULA

This region includes the counties of Cornwall, Devon, and Somerset, and the western part of Dorset. The *relief of the land* may be related to the various types of rock. In Cornwall and Devon the chief hill masses—Dartmoor, Bodmin Moor, and Land's End—are made of granite; Exmoor, in Somerset, is composed of hard slates and sandstone belonging to the Old Red Sandstone system; and the Mendip Hills, which may be taken as the northern boundary of the region, are composed of carboniferous limestone similar to that which makes the northern Pennines. The lowlands of Cornwall and Devon are composed of various types of sandstone and shales among which red is the predominant colour. In Somerset and eastern Devon is a north-to-south strip of soft New Red Sandstone, which forms the plains around Taunton and Exeter and sends a tongue up the Vale of Crediton.

The *river system* is somewhat peculiar, in that only the minor streams radiate from the central mass of Dartmoor. The Tamar and the Exe flow almost across the peninsula from north to south, and the Torridge, which rises near the Tamar, doubles back upon itself and flows to the north coast of Devon.

Climate

The outstanding features of the climate of the south-western peninsula may be related to its relief and position. It is fully exposed to the south-westerly winds, which must

Will F. Taylor

RIVER DART, DARTMOOR

Will F. Taylor

THE NEEDLES, ISLE OF WIGHT

rise on encountering the high land, thus causing abundant rain in all seasons. The winter temperatures are remarkably mild, the coastal lowlands being several degrees warmer in January than any other part of Britain. Snow rarely lies long even on Dartmoor, and is very rare on the south coast, where palms of subtropical appearance flourish in sheltered places. This remarkable mildness of the winters is due to: (a) the southerly latitude, which gives the region longer winter days and greater sun force than areas farther north; (b) exposure to the warm south-westerly winds and the warm Gulf Stream; (c) shelter from the cold northerly and easterly winds.

In summer the average temperature is slightly lower than that of central and south-eastern England, since the south-westerly winds are relatively cool in this season, and the peninsula is usually outside the influence of the anticyclones which cause eastern England to have long spells of dry, cold weather in winter, and long spells of dry, hot weather in summer.

OCCUPATIONS OF THE PEOPLE

The occupations of the people are to a large extent determined by the physical geography of the peninsula.

Farming is the chief industry, since the peninsula is lacking in coal and iron, and is remote from great centres of population. *Sheep* are reared on Dartmoor, Exmoor, and other areas of high land, but the pasture is so poor that the number of sheep per square mile is small. *Cattle* are the chief interest of the farmers on the lowlands, since the mild, moist climate favours the growth of meadow grass and fodder crops. Devonshire specializes in the raising of young stock, which are sent to the Midlands and other districts for fattening.

Cornwall and Somerset are noted for dairy farming, but the distance from large centres of population has resulted in the specialization in butter, cheese, and preserved cream, rather than in fresh milk for daily distribution.

Arable farming is directed chiefly to the production of food-stuffs for the cattle. Oats, roots, and rotation grasses are the chief crops, though small quantities of wheat and barley are grown in valleys deep in the rain-shadow of the hills.

Fruit-growing and *market gardening* are encouraged by the mild winter, early spring, and sunny summer. Devon and Somerset are famous for the production of cider apples, but the moist climate permits the spread of fungoid diseases which have caused a considerable diminution in the crops in recent years. The Scilly Isles and the coastal districts of western Cornwall specialize in the production of spring flowers and early vegetables. Winter frosts are almost unknown in this district and the January temperature is about as high as the April temperature in north-western England. Consequently narcissi, daffodils, and other spring flowers are in full bloom in the Scilly Isles when plants in northern England are just showing their leaves above the ground.

Fishing. The coast of Cornwall is of the ria type, i.e. the land has sunk a little so that the sea has flowed into the lower parts of the valleys, forming long, many-branched inlets, which provide excellent harbours for fishing vessels. Cornwall is near the southern limit of the cold-water fishes, such as herring, and near the northern boundary of warm-water fishes, of which the pilchard may be taken as an example. The variety of fish caught is therefore remarkable; but in spite of this the fishing industry is not in a flourishing condition, since (*a*) Cornwall is a long way from the great centres of population which form the chief markets; (*b*) there are no great fishing-grounds comparable to the Dogger Bank and other areas in the North Sea; (c) the fishing boats and the fishing ports are small, and the industry has not attracted the capital necessary to enable it to compete with that of the North Sea.

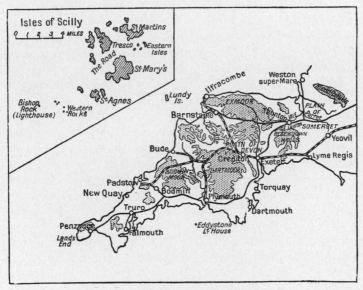

FIG. 50. THE SOUTH-WESTERN PENINSULA

The Tourist Industry. We have seen that Cornwall markets her oceanic climate in the form of spring flowers and vegetables; she also derives profit from her beautiful scenery, which attracts many thousands of visitors in every season of the year. The Cornish coast is sometimes spoken of as the 'English Riviera,' on account of the mildness of its winters. Many of the old fishing villages such as Looe and St Ives have become popular holiday centres, and the tourist industry more than compensates for the decline of the fishing

Mining. More than two thousand years ago Cornwall was famous for its tin ore, and until the middle of last century it remained the world's chief source of tin. Though the Cornish supplies of tin are by no means exhausted, the ore can be mined more cheaply in Malaya, Bolivia, Nigeria, and other places, and so most of the Cornish mines have had to close down, though some are worked when the world price of of tin is high. The former chief centres of the tin-mining industry are Camborne and Redruth.

The chief mineral now obtained from Cornwall is kaolin, or china clay, a fine white clay which is formed when granite decays. The chief areas of production, such as the St Austell and upper Fal districts, are situated on the edges of the granite masses, where transport to the coast is easy.

Most of the kaolin is sent to the Potteries, where it is used in the manufacture of fine porcelain and pottery, but large quantities are also used for making the 'size' in which cotton yarn is dipped before it is woven, and for the 'filling' which gives the smooth, white surface to writing paper. As the clay is a bulky product which does not deteriorate through being a long time in transit, most of it is sent out by sea to the Mersey estuary, whence it is sent by canal to the Potteries or to the cotton towns of Lancashire. Small quantities of so-called 'ball-clay,' which is also used in the pottery industry, are obtained in Devonshire. Some of it is used in the small local pottery industry, but most of it is sent to north Staffordshire.

Manufacturing. Before the Industrial Revolution the south-western peninsula was an important centre of the woollen industry, and there are still small woollen factories at Ashburton and Buckfastleigh.

RAILWAYS AND TOWNS

The south-western peninsula is served by two main lines of railway which, prior to nationalization, were known as the Southern Railway and the Great Western. The former enters the region in the eastern corner of Devon. Beyond

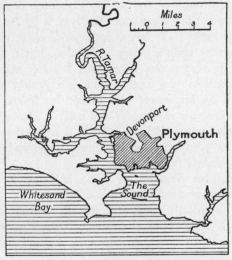

FIG. 51. THE POSITION OF PLYMOUTH

Exeter the main line skirts the northern and western sides of Dartmoor to its terminus at Plymouth, while branch lines run to Ilfracombe and Padstow. The former Great Western Railway runs through Taunton and Exeter, and round the southern side of Dartmoor to Plymouth, and thence to Falmouth and Penzance.

Exeter, the county town of Devonshire, is situated in the middle of a fertile plain, and at the former head of navigation of the River Exe. Its name implies that it was a Roman

military station; its cathedral indicates that it was a prosperous city in the Middle Ages; and its large cattle market
and its manufactures of agricultural implements show that it
is the market for the rich farm lands around.

Taunton is an important railway centre, and the market
for the fertile New Red Sandstone Vale of Taunton.

Plymouth, situated at the head of Plymouth Sound between
the estuaries of the Tamar and the Plym, is by far the largest
town of the region.   It has a deep, landlocked, ria harbour,
and has express train services to London, but it suffers as a
port from its remoteness from both London and the great
industrial centres.   Its foreign trade is therefore very small,
though it is an important port of call for liners which dis-
charge and embark passengers and mails.   *Devonport*, which
is now amalgamated with Plymouth, is a naval station, and
much of the prosperity of the town is dependent on the
naval dockyards situated there.

Falmouth, also situated on a ria harbour, is a holiday
centre, a fishing station, and a minor port.

Bodmin, the county town of Cornwall, is situated on a low
pass through which runs the railway from *Fowey*, a kaolin
port on the south coast, to *Padstow*, a small fishing town
on the opposite coast of Cornwall.

EXAMINATION QUESTIONS

1. Show to what extent the various occupations of the inhabitants
of either Devonshire or Lincolnshire are influenced by geographical
conditions. (C. L.)

2. Draw a sketch-map to show the areas of moorland that are found
in the peninsula of south-west England.   Write a description of *one*

of these regions from the point of view of (*a*) the relief; (*b*) the vegetation; (*c*) the occupations of the people.   (D. M.)

3. Explain the geographical factors that account for the greater density of population in *either* south Lancashire as compared with Cheshire *or* south Staffordshire as compared with Cornwall.

Discuss geographically *two* of the main industries in the regions you compare.   (L. M.)

4. With the aid of a sketch-map, show how the major relief features of the south-west peninsula *or* the Pennines have determined the main lines of communication.   Name and describe the principal route centres and passes.   (D. M.)

5. Discuss the importance for industrial purposes of Dartmoor, the Cleveland Hills, and the Pennines.   (O. S. C.)

CHAPTER XII

THE HAMPSHIRE BASIN AND THE CHANNEL ISLANDS

The Hampshire Basin

THIS region includes not only the county of Hampshire, of which the Isle of Wight is a part, but also the greater part of Dorset. The term 'basin' is descriptive of both the structure and the relief. The same layer of chalk which forms the Chilterns and the North and South Downs, is here bent downwards in the form of a shallow, oval dish, which has been broken in places and partially filled with sand and clay. On the northern edge of the basin the chalk rock is almost horizontal, and crops out as the plateau known as Salisbury Plain. On the southern side the chalk is almost vertical, and forms the narrow ridge which runs through the Isle of Wight and the so-called 'Isle' of Purbeck. The eastern and western edges of the basin are formed by the South Downs and the Dorset Heights respectively.

Ages ago this chalk basin was entirely submerged, and gradually covered by deposits of sand and mud and lime. Uplift then took place, and the deposits were washed from the edges of the chalk and deposited in the middle of the basin, on top of the earlier marine deposits. Later, the land sank again, and the sea cut through the rim of chalk, thus forming the Solent and Spithead. When this last partial submergence took place the lower courses of the river valleys were 'drowned,' so that the present river system of the Hampshire basin may be described as 'fragmentary' (see

Fig. 52). When the whole basin was above sea-level the main river was the Frome, the present straits of the Solent and Spithead were the lower portion of its valley, and the Rivers Stour, Avon, Test, and Itchen were tributaries.

The sea is still attacking and destroying the wall of chalk

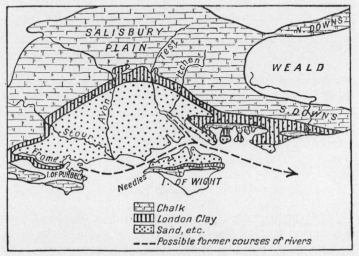

FIG. 52. THE HAMPSHIRE BASIN—GEOLOGICAL

which forms the southern rim of the basin. The bold promontory of the Needles, which is the seaward end of the chalk backbone of the Isle of Wight, terminates in a series of isolated pinnacles or stacks, which, quite obviously, were once parts of the main ridge. Similar stacks are to be seen off the coast of the Isle of Purbeck, and old maps mark the positions of some which have now entirely disappeared. Eventually all the present stacks will be washed away, and others will be formed as the sea eats into the softer parts of the cliffs, leaving the harder parts standing out in temporary defiance of the waves. On the south coast of Dorset the sea has cut through the thin wall of rock (not chalk in this case), and hollowed

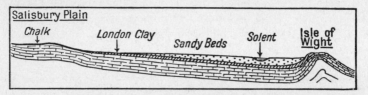

FIG. 53. GEOLOGICAL SECTION ACROSS THE HAMPSHIRE BASIN

out deep coves, of which Lulworth Cove is the most magnificent. In the distant future such coves and bays will become so large and numerous that no more than a few isolated rocks will be left to mark the position of the present coastline.

FARMING

The Hampshire basin produces no minerals, and the region is therefore devoted almost entirely to farming. Methods of farming vary according to the types of rock and soil. The chalk lands are, as we have seen (page 26), usually most suitable for wheat-growing and sheep-rearing, and this type of farming predominates on Salisbury Plain and other chalk lands of the northern rim of the basin. Four types of land may be noted, viz.:

(1) Pasture lands with very thin soil.

(2) The chalky upland, where arable now replaces much of the former grassland. Since 1939 the number of sheep has been halved and the acreage of wheat and barley more than doubled.

(3) The lower hill slopes, which are typical mixed farming areas.

(4) The valley floors, which are covered with fertile alluvial soil, and are sufficiently moist to specialize in dairying.

During the present century the downland farmers have also increased their stocks of cattle at the expense of the sheep, and dairying is now more important than sheep-rearing

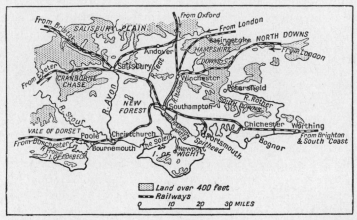

FIG. 54. THE HAMPSHIRE BASIN—PHYSICAL, TOWNS, AND RAILWAYS

except in those parts where there are large areas of chalk with soil so thin that neither crops nor meadow grass can be grown.

The lowlands within the basin are composed of a great variety of rocks and soils—clay, pebbles, sand, and lime. The layer of clay which occurs just above the chalk and just within the chalk rim, forms fertile arable land, and is devoted chiefly to dairying, as are the fertile alluvial lands of the valley bottoms. Over most of the basin, however, the soil is sandy and infertile, and large areas have never been cleared. Such an area is the New Forest, once famous as a royal hunting-ground, and now a favourite resort of tourists and holiday-makers. The natural forest consists largely of oak, ash, and other deciduous trees, but large areas have been planted with pine trees in modern times. There are also extensive stretches of heathland which, though entirely useless for farming, add greatly to the scenic beauty of the area.

In modern times there has been a considerable development of market gardening and fruit-growing on some of the sandy lands which had formerly been considered worthless. The reasons for this development are:

(1) The climate is very sunny and rather dry, and spring is warmer and earlier than in districts farther north.

(2) The sandy soil is easily worked, and can be fertilized with the addition of artificial manures.

(3) The growth of residential towns has provided a local market for fruit and vegetables, while the express train services between Southampton and the densely peopled parts of the country, though instituted primarily to serve the passenger traffic of the port, give easy access to more distant markets.

ROUTES AND TOWNS

Most of the towns of the Hampshire basin are peripheral, i.e. arranged round the edge of the region. Two groups of such peripheral towns may be recognized, viz.:

(1) Those situated in gaps in the chalk rim. *Winchester*, situated on a hilly site overlooking the valley of the Itchen and at the junction of six Roman roads, controls the chief route from London to Southampton. It was the Anglo-Saxon capital of Wessex, and, as the kings of Wessex became kings of England, it was in a sense the capital of the country. It is now a market town, and is noted for its fine cathedral, which is the longest in Britain.

Salisbury, the county town of Wiltshire, is situated where the River Avon provides a route through the chalk rim of the basin. Near by is the prehistoric fortress of Old Sarum. Other peripheral gap towns are *Petersfield*, *Whitchurch*, and *Andover*.

(2) *Coastal towns.* These fall into three groups, viz.: ancient ports, naval stations, and modern residential towns. To the first class belong *Christchurch*, situated on the estuary of the combined Rivers Stour and Avon, and *Poole*, situated on the broad but shallow Poole Harbour. Neither is now of any commercial importance as a port. The two naval stations are *Portsmouth* and *Weymouth*. The former is the most strongly forti-

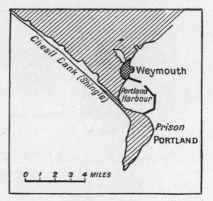

FIG. 55. WEYMOUTH AND THE 'ISLE' OF PORTLAND

fied place in the British Isles. It has a large naval dockyard, and is important for marine and general engineering. Its population is a quarter of a million and it is by far the largest town in the Hampshire basin. *Weymouth* is a minor naval station, a packet station, and holiday resort. Near by, on the so-called Isle of Portland (really a peninsula joined to the mainland by a bank of pebbles), are the quarries from which the famous Portland building-stone is obtained.

Of the residential and holiday resorts, *Bournemouth* is by far the largest. It has the advantages of an exceptionally mild climate, sandy soil, southerly aspect, fine cliffs, and beautiful woodlands.

Southampton is the fifth port of Britain in respect of the total value of its trade, the third port in respect of the tonnage of vessels using its harbour, and the first in respect of its passenger traffic. It owes its importance to its position and to the way in which men have utilized its natural advantages. It is situated nearly at the centre of the Hampshire basin,

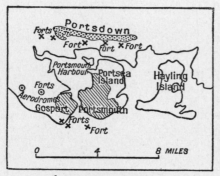

FIG. 56. POSITION OF PORTSMOUTH

at the natural focus of routes through the chalk rim, and at the head of the deep, sheltered inlet of Southampton Water. In addition it has two advantages which distinguish it from other British ports: it is situated on a peninsula between the mouths of two rivers—the Test and the Itchen—so that it has a double water-front, and it has four high tides a day. It is often said that this latter phenomenon is due to the wave of the tide being split by the projecting corner of the Isle of Wight, so that one branch goes up the Solent while the other goes round the Isle of Wight and up Spithead, arriving at Southampton two hours later than the first branch. As other Channel ports have the same double tides, it seems, however, that the phenomenon is due to some more general cause, such as the gradual narrowing of the Channel. Whatever their cause, the double tides are of great value to Southampton, as there is no really low tide between them and vessels can enter the harbour at all times.

Other advantages of Southampton are that it is in a good

position for trading with the Channel ports of France, and that it can 'short circuit' the traffic to London.

The express train services which were instituted primarily to serve the passenger and mail traffic have attracted to the port a great volume of trade in perishable goods, such as meat and fruit, and in recent years there has also been a great increase in general imports destined for London and the Midlands.

At Fawley, near Southampton, is one of the world's greatest oil depots and oil 'cracking' plants.

THE CHANNEL ISLANDS

These islands, which lie off the coast of Normandy, are the oldest possession of the British crown. They were part of William the Conqueror's Dukedom of Normandy, and still owe allegiance to the King of England as representative of the Duke of Normandy. The people are of Norman stock, and the official language is French, though English is taught in the schools and used in business. By an ancient treaty the islanders are exempted from all taxes levied in England, and as both local taxes and customs duties are very low, the

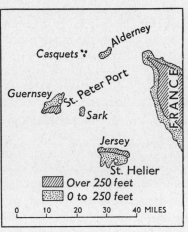

FIG. 57. CHANNEL ISLANDS

islands have attracted some wealthy residents from England.

The four largest islands are Jersey, Guernsey, Alderney,

and Sark. For administrative purposes Alderney and Sark are included with Guernsey, while Jersey is a separate unit.

The chief economic advantage possessed by the islands is their southerly latitude, which gives them milder winters and earlier springs than Britain. As a consequence, market gardening is the chief occupation of the people. Jersey is particularly noted for early potatoes and for vegetables which are planted in May, after the soil has been cleared of potatoes. Guernsey, on the other hand, specializes in tomatoes and flowers, most of which are grown under glass. The reason for this difference in specialization is that the slope of the land in Jersey is from north to south, so that it gets the maximum amount of sunshine, while in Guernsey the land slopes away from the sun.

Jersey, Guernsey, and Alderney have each produced a special breed of cattle, the Jersey cattle in particular being noted for the richness of their milk.

St Helier, on the south coast of Jersey, is the chief town and port of the islands.

EXAMINATION QUESTIONS

1. Compare the physical features and climate of (a) the Hampshire basin and (b) the Vale of York, and show how these have affected the agriculture and pastoral occupations in each. Where in each case do the farmers seek their chief markets? (C. S. C.)

2. Describe the physical features and the distribution of population of *either* the Hampshire basin *or* the Lake District. (D. M.)

Will F. Taylor

HOP-PICKERS IN KENT

Will F. Taylor

THE SEVEN SISTERS, SUSSEX

CHAPTER XIII

SOUTH-EASTERN ENGLAND

THIS region lies between the Hampshire basin and the coast of the Dover Strait, and between the lower Thames and the Channel coast, and includes the counties of Surrey, Kent, and Sussex. The dominant physical features are the chalk escarpments of the North and South Downs, which diverge from Salisbury Plain and form a horseshoe-shaped frame for the area. Within this horseshoe are almost level clay vales, which in their turn enclose the central hill mass of the Forest Range.

STRUCTURE

Ages ago the rocks of this region were pushed up to form an elongated dome which stretched from Salisbury Plain into Belgium and north-eastern France. At first the chalk formed a continuous cover to the dome, but in the course of ages the weather and the streams wore away the central and more elevated portion, thus exposing the rocks below the chalk. At the same time subsidence and the action of the sea formed the Strait of Dover, which now separates the British from the continental portion of the dome.

The block diagram (Fig. 58) shows that the elevation of the land is determined by the hardness of the rock. As already pointed out, chalk and sandstone are resistant to weathering because they are not only fairly hard rocks, but are also porous, so that the water runs through them

Clay, on the other hand, is relatively soft, and as it is impervious the water remains on the surface and quickly wears

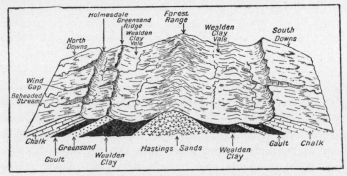

FIG. 58. THE WEALD—BLOCK DIAGRAM

it away. In the region under consideration the rocks dip outwards from the central ridge, and hard and soft rocks are arranged alternately (see Figs. 58 and 59). The central

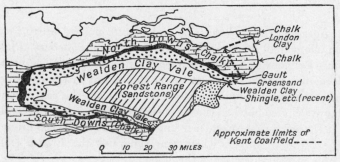

FIG. 59. SOUTH-EASTERN ENGLAND—GEOLOGICAL

Forest Range, which reaches a height of 804 feet in Crowborough Beacon, is formed chiefly of sandstone known as the Hastings Sands. Around the Forest Range is the horseshoe-shaped vale formed of Wealdon Clay. These two divisions

comprise the district known as the Weald, though sometimes the term is used to designate the whole area between
the North and South Downs. The layer of Greensand forms
a prominent ridge on the northern side of the Wealden
Clay Vale, but on the southern side it is very thin and forms
no prominent feature. Between the Greensand ridge and the
North Downs is the Gault Clay Vale, which is sometimes
known as the Vale of Holmesdale. On the southern side the
corresponding belt of Gault Clay merges into the Wealden
Clay Vale. The North and South Downs are inward-facing
escarpments, with the steep scarp slopes overlooking the
Vale of Holmesdale and the Wealden Clay Vale respectively.
In east Kent the formerly detached area which is still known
as the Isle of Thanet is formed by a subsidiary fold in the
layer of chalk.

The features of the sea-coast are the counterpart of those
of the land. The bold headlands of North Foreland, South
Foreland, and Beachy Head mark the points where the chalk
ridges run out to sea; and the smooth, unindented coast
between these headlands is due to the low elevation of the
land at these places. Dungeness, which seems so prominent
on an outline map, is not a headland, but merely an accumulation of sand and shingle which has been built up within
historic times.

THE RIVER SYSTEM

As might be expected, the Forest Range forms the chief
watershed, and rivers flow from it northward to the Thames
and southward to the Channel coast, breaking through the
wall of the Downs in deep gaps. They do not, however,
flow due north or south, but follow zigzag courses, with two
or more right-angle bends (note, for example, the Medway

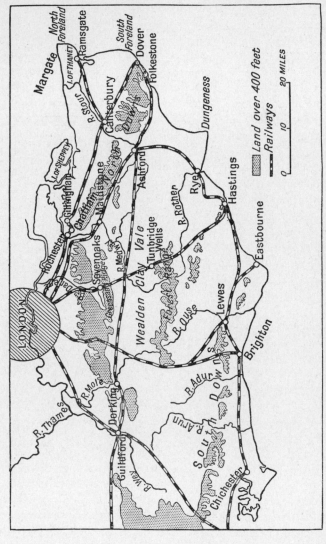

FIG. 60. SOUTH-EASTERN ENGLAND—PHYSICAL, TOWNS, AND RAILWAYS

which flows for the greater part of its course almost due eastwards through the Wealden Clay Vale). The story of

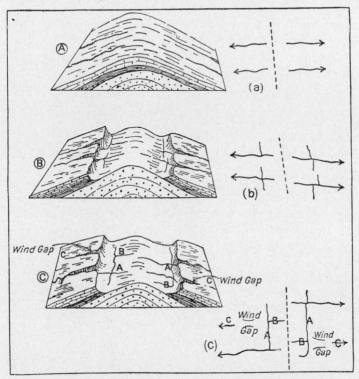

FIG. 61. BLOCK DIAGRAMS ILLUSTRATING RIVER CAPTURE AND THE DEVELOPMENT OF ESCARPMENTS

the development of these rivers, and of the formation of the gaps in the chalk, is of great interest. When the dome was first formed the original rivers would flow north and south from the central ridge (Fig. 61A). As the land was gradually worn down by the weather, the escarpments of hard rock began to show up like the grain on an old school desk, while the rivers went on cutting down through the ridges, like so many saws (see Fig. 61B). In the meantime, however, tributaries began to develop in the clay vales, and some of these 'captured' the head-streams of the neighbouring rivers. Thus in Fig. 61C, stream A has captured stream B, leaving C as a beheaded stream opposite a 'wind gap' through the escarpment.

Farming in South-eastern England

As in other districts the types of farming are controlled by the relief and soil, which in their turn are determined by the types of rock. In view of what has been said above concerning the variety of rocks in the region, it is not surprising to find that the type of farming varies considerably from place to place. The sandstones of the central *Forest Range* are naturally infertile, and the higher parts are given up to heath and woodland, though there is some rather poor pasture in the lower portions. The very name *Weald* is a reminder of its infertility, for it is derived from an Anglo-Saxon word meaning woodland or waste. On account of the infertility of the soil and the thickness of the forest, the High Weald was for long a boundary zone between those Anglo-Saxon tribes who advanced southward from the Thames valley and those who came northward from the coast, and it is for this reason, rather than because of the elevation of the land, that the centre of the Weald is the boundary between Surrey and Kent on the north and Sussex on the south.

The *Wealden Clay* is naturally fertile, but its water-holding properties make it more suitable for grass than for grain, and as the region is situated fairly near London, it specializes in the production of milk.

The *Greensand Hills*, to the north of the Wealden Clay

Vale, resemble the Forest Range in their general infertility, and are largely covered with heath and poor pasture.

The *Gault Clay Vale* is another dairying area, with much of the land under plough, and with very fertile strips on the edges, where the soil is mixed with chalk or sand.

FIG. 62. THE HOP-GROWING DISTRICTS OF THE SOUTH-EAST
(Intensity of shading roughly proportional to the production)

The *South Downs* are still important for sheep, as there is only a thin layer of soil above the chalk. The springy character of the turf has also made this area one of the chief breeding- and training-grounds for racehorses and hunters. On the lowlands the chief cereal is oats, and 'Sussex ground oats' are prized by farmers all over the country. On the *North Downs* there are extensive deposits of clay overlying the chalk, and consequently a much greater proportion of the land is under plough than is the case on the South Downs.

Fruit and *hops* are grown chiefly on the lowlands of Kent, where there are rich mixed soils. Hops are grown chiefly on the valley floors, where the rich, mixed soil is

underlain by clay. Much labour and skill is needed for the cultivation of hops, and the industry is one of the most intensive
types of farming known anywhere in the world. The ground
requires frequent forking, manuring, and weeding; the plants
must be sprayed from time to time to keep them clear of
vermin, and elaborate supports must be provided for the
'vines.' Formerly chestnut poles were used as supports, but
these are now generally replaced by lengths of coir yarn
attached to a network of overhead wires supported by poles
thirteen or fourteen feet high. For the hop-picking, which
takes place in September, the local labour supply is quite
insufficient, and thousands of men, women, and children
migrate temporarily from the East End of London to the
hop-fields, where they are accommodated in sheds or
temporary camps.

Fruit is grown chiefly on light, mixed soils which have a
foundation of rock to provide good drainage. Most of the
orchards are situated on slightly rising ground, as experience
has shown that such land suffers less from frost than the
flat valley floors. Kent contains about a quarter of the total
area of orchard in England, and about the same fraction of
the total area planted with small fruits, such as currants,
gooseberries, strawberries, and raspberries. Apples, plums,
and cherries are the chief orchard fruits.

Market gardening is carried on chiefly in the lower Medway
valley, which has the great advantage of proximity to the
London markets.

MINING

Iron ore occurs in beds of clay in the Forest Range, and in
the days when charcoal was used for smelting, the Weald
was one of the chief iron-mining and smelting districts in the

country. After the Industrial Revolution, however, the absence of local coal caused the decay of the industry, and now neither iron-mining nor smelting is carried on there.

Coal. The east Kent coal-field is unique among the coal-fields of the British Isles in that it is entirely concealed by newer rocks. Borings made through the chalk have shown that the coal-field has an area of about two hundred square miles, the northern limit of workable coal being situated near Ramsgate, and the western limit near Canterbury (see Fig. 63). The three collieries at present in operation produce about one million tons a year, much of which is dispatched to the port of Dover. Rich deposits of iron ore are also known to exist within the area of the coal-field, and so it seems reasonable to expect that there will some day be a revival of the iron-smelting industry in this region.

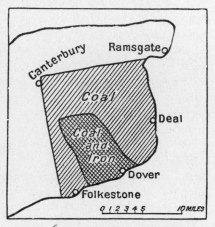

FIG. 63. THE KENT COAL-FIELD

(N.B. The coal-measures are concealed by the chalk)

TOWN SITES

Gap Towns are situated where the rivers break through the North and South Downs, good examples being Guildford on the Wey, Dorking on the Mole, Lewes on the Sussex

* F

Ouse, and Arundel on the Arun. At the eastern end of the North Downs the gap towns are arranged in pairs, one at each end of the gap, e.g. Ashford and Canterbury on the Stour, Maidstone and Rochester on the Medway. The gap towns are the natural foci of routes, and many of them owe their early importance to the building of castles around which the trading population congregated for safety. In modern times the building of railways and the proximity to London have encouraged the growth of miscellaneous industries, among which may be mentioned the manufacture of bricks, cement, and steam-rollers at Rochester.

Canterbury, situated at the former head of navigation on the River Stour, and at the focus of land routes from the coast, was an important port in Roman and pre-Roman times. In Anglo-Saxon times it was the capital of the kingdom of Kent, and has been the ecclesiastical capital of the country since the introduction of Christianity in the sixth and seventh centuries.

Inland Residential Centres. Among the factors which determine the growth of residential centres are accessibility, porous subsoil, and beautiful scenery. All these advantages are to be found on the North Downs, the Greensand Hills, and the Forest Range, and in these districts there are many residential centres which may be regarded as outlying suburbs of London. On the higher parts of the North Downs the lack of water has been a great difficulty, but there are now many large estates and small residential towns to which water is pumped from the valleys. On the Greensand Hills the largest town is Sevenoaks, situated opposite the Darent gap through the chalk ridge. In the Forest Range is Tunbridge Wells, which owed its rise to medicinal springs discovered there in 1606.

Ports. In medieval times the chief links between Britain and the Continent were the *Cinque Ports*. The five original 'head ports' were Sandwich, Dover, Hythe, Romney, and Hastings, but to these were added Winchelsea and Rye, and many smaller ports. For several hundred years these ports had almost a monopoly of the trade with the Continent, and in return for the special privileges they had to provide the kings of England with ships and sailors in time of war. Nowadays all these ancient harbours, with the exception of that of Dover, which is situated in a deep cleft in the chalk hills, are silted up and useless for commerce.

Modern *packet stations*, from which express train services run to London, are Dover, Folkestone, and Newhaven.

Coastal holiday resorts and residential towns are very numerous. The largest is Brighton, which has the advantages of being nearest to London and of having the beautiful South Downs as a background.

EXAMINATION QUESTIONS

1. England south of the Thames may be divided into three principal natural regions: the west country, the Hampshire basin, and the chalk and Wealden area. Locate these divisions, and point out how the physical geography affects the occupations of the people. (L. M.)

2. Choose four towns in south-east England (not including London), and analyse their sites in relation to the relief and main lines of communication. (L. M.)

3. Compare and contrast the geographical conditions in the south-western peninsula of England with those in south-eastern England (approximately Kent, Surrey, and Sussex). (L. G. S.)

4. Show the important influences of the geological structure and the character of the rocks on the land forms of *either* South Wales *or* that part of south-east England which lies between the lower Thames and the English Channel. (W. M.)

CHAPTER XIV

THE THAMES BASIN

A RIVER basin is the area drained by that river and its tributaries, and the watershed, or divide, is the line bounding the basin, and dividing it from neighbouring river basins.

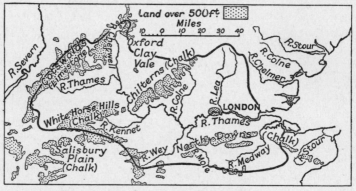

FIG. 64.   THE THAMES BASIN

A watershed is often compared to the ridge of a roof, since the water drains from it in opposite directions; but the watershed is not always situated on high land, nor are the slopes from it always very obvious.   Moreover, the river basin often includes land which is higher than any point of the watershed. The watershed of the Thames, for example (see Fig. 64), passes over the high land of the Wealden Forest Range and the Cotswold Hills, and also across the low vale between the Cotswolds and the Chilterns and the almost level plain of Essex,

156

while within the basin are such prominent escarpments as the Chilterns and the North Downs.

The chalk escarpments divide the Thames basin into three clearly marked natural regions, viz.:

(1) The northern half of the Weald, which has been dealt with in the preceding chapter.

(2) The London basin, or lower Thames basin, which lies between the Chilterns and the North Downs.

(3) The upper Thames basin, between the Cotswolds on the North-west and the Chilterns and the Marlborough Downs on the south-east.

THE UPPER THAMES BASIN

This region comprises the oolitic limestone and the chalk escarpments, with the Oxford Clay Vale between them (see Fig. 4).

The *Cotswold Hills* consist chiefly of limestone, but there is generally a sufficient depth of soil to make arable farming profitable, and there are now few areas given up entirely to sheep. On the very fertile, well-drained soils of the lower slopes and valleys arable farming and dairying predominate. Many of the small towns of the southern Cotswolds were formerly noted for the manufacture of woollen goods (see page 115), and Witney in Oxfordshire still manufactures blankets.

The *Oxford Clay Vale* contains belts of fertile loam, as well as large areas of heavy clay soils. The latter are chiefly devoted to cattle-rearing, the Vale of Aylesbury being one of the most notable dairying regions in Britain. On the lighter soils, where there is some of the best farm land in the country, there has been in recent years a great increase in the area under wheat.

Oxford is situated on a low ridge between the Thames and

its tributary the Cherwell.   Its situation at an easy crossing-place of the Thames, and at the focus of roads and river routes helps to account for the early growth of its famous university. *Cowley*, a few miles to the south-east of the city, is now world famous for the manufacture of the Morris cars.

Swindon is situated at the head of the Vale of White Horse, which lies north of White Horse Hill and the Marlborough Downs.   Originally a small market town, it owes its modern growth to its selection by the G.W.R. Co. as its chief centre for the manufacture of locomotives and rolling stock.

The London Basin

This region, like the corresponding Hampshire basin, is formed by a downfold of the chalk.   On the northern edge of the basin the rocks are almost horizontal, and the chalk outcrop forms the comparatively broad belt of the Chiltern

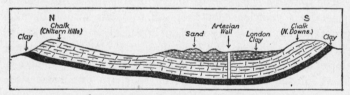

FIG. 65. SECTION ACROSS THE LONDON BASIN

Hills, while on the southern edge of the basin the chalk rises much more steeply, forming the comparatively narrow ridge of the North Downs.   The basin itself is partially filled in with a variety of rocks which represent the sediments deposited in a former semi-inland sea.   Immediately above the chalk, and forming a narrow strip of undulating country around the edge of the basin, are the Woolwich and Reading beds, which are composed chiefly of the pebbles deposited on the ancient sea beach. Where these pebbly beds outcrop the soil is naturally infertile, and much of the land has never been cultivated, but has been left as commons and open spaces. Among these the most famous is Blackheath, south of Greenwich. As a wild and desolate tract crossed by the main road from Dover to London it was formerly the haunt of highwaymen. Though much of it has now been built on, a large

FIG. 66. LONDON BASIN—GEOLOGICAL

part still remains as a public common. In the north-west of the London basin similar pebbly beds form a low escarpment running parallel to the Chilterns and overlooking the upper courses of the Rivers Lea and Colne.

The *London Clay* lies above the Woolwich and Reading beds, and occupies the greater part of the basin. Three interesting geographical effects of the clay may be noted: (*a*) the clay lands formerly grew much wheat for the London market, but are now devoted chiefly to the production of fresh milk; (*b*) the existence of the thick bed of clay facilitated the boring of the underground railways which are such a characteristic feature of London; (*c*) the clay has also made possible the boring of numerous artesian wells. Rain which falls on the North Downs and the Chilterns soaks into the porous chalk, and is there imprisoned between the impervious Gault Clay below and the London Clay above. Borings put down through the London Clay into the chalk tap this underground supply, and the water is forced up the bore by the pressure of water percolating from the sides of the basin. Such artesian wells are used chiefly to supply factories and breweries, most of London's domestic supply being obtained from reservoirs situated near the Thames.

The *Bagshot Sands* and other sandy beds occur above the London Clay, but are found only in isolated patches which form the summits of low hills. As these sandy lands are dry and infertile they have been largely left as uncultivated commons and heaths, some of which have in modern times been chosen as the sites of residential suburbs such as Hampstead, Harrow, and Elstree.

Alluvium, which is the most recent of the deposits, occupies the lower parts of the valleys of the Thames and its tributaries. Formerly these alluvial lowlands were too marshy for settlement, but modern pumping and drainage schemes have made it possible to use these lands for building purposes.

THE RIVER SYSTEM

The *Thames* breaks through the chalk scarp which forms the boundary between the upper Thames basin and the London basin, by the Goring Gap, some ten miles above Reading. Below this point the river meanders across its flood-plain in wide curves which cut into the chalk at Marlow on the northern side, and at Windsor and Greenhythe on the southern side. The *Kennet*, which joins the Thames at Reading, may be regarded as the axial stream of the London

Topical Press

LONDON—WHITEHALL AND TRAFALGAR SQUARE FROM THE AIR

basin, since it follows fairly closely the axis of the down-fold. Other right-bank tributaries—the Wey, the Mole, the Darent, and the Medway—flow from the Wealden uplift, and have already been dealt with on page 147. The left-bank tributaries, of which the chief are the Colne and the Lea, rise in the Chilterns and the low chalk hills which lie on the borders of Hertfordshire and Bedfordshire. Ages ago tributaries probably flowed from the Cotswolds through the Chilterns direct to the lower Thames; but the Thame, cutting back its head in the Oxford Clay at the foot of the scarp slope of the Chilterns, beheaded these streams and diverted their waters into the Thames above the Goring Gap. The former course of such beheaded streams may still be traced in the numerous dry valleys which notch the Chilterns and provide easy routes through them (see Fig. 68). The rivers of Essex and Suffolk —the Crouch, the Chelmer, the Colne, the Stour, and the Orwell—may be regarded as former tributaries of the Thames which have been converted into separate rivers by the drowning of the lower portion of the basin.

In and around London several small streams rise at the junction of the London Clay and the overlying sandy beds. Among these are the Holborn, Westbourne, Tyburn, and Walbrook, all of which, though now covered in, gave their names to parts of London.

LONDON

The factors which account for the origin and growth of London may be summarized as follows:

(1) It is situated at the lowest easy crossing-place of the Thames, where firm ground comes within a short distance of either bank.

(2) On the northern bank two low hills, protected on east

and west by marshy valleys, facilitated defence of the river crossing.

(3) It is situated at the highest point which can be reached by sea-going vessels.

(4) It is the centre of the road and railway systems of the country.

(5) The great rise of the tide (twenty feet at London Bridge) enables all but the largest ocean steamers to use the port.

(6) The estuary opens on the busiest corner of the busiest sea in the world.

(7) As the capital and chief port of Britain, its development has kept pace with the growth of British trade and with the development of the British Commonwealth

(8) The ease of assemblage of raw materials, and the facilities for the distribution of manufactured goods, have made it the foremost manufacturing city in the world.

(9) As the world's chief centre of banking and finance it is the principal 'market' for almost every type of raw material and manufactured goods.

(10) Its pre-eminence in world commerce has made it a great *entrepôt*, i.e. a port at which goods are collected for distribution over a wide area for export in bulk.

London as a Port

The Port of London includes the whole of the tidal portion of the Thames from the open sea to the tidal limit at Teddington, a distance of nearly seventy miles. London Bridge is, however, the limit of sea navigation, and consequently all foreign commerce is confined to the part below the bridge. Vessels drawing ten to fourteen feet of water can navigate the 'pools' which lie between the Tower Bridge and Limehouse, but larger vessels are accommodated in the

docks which line the river between Limehouse Reach and
Gallions Reach (see Fig. 67). *Gravesend*, which is a part of
the Port of London, is the point where sea pilots are exchanged
for river pilots. It owes its rise to the fact that the deep-
water channel there swings to the southern bank of the river,
where firm ground comes close to the water front. *Tilbury*,

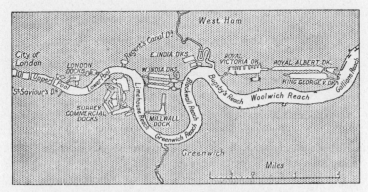

FIG. 67. THE LONDON DOCKS

immediately opposite Gravesend, and twenty-four miles from
the open sea, is the great passenger depot of the Port of
London. It is equipped with fine modern docks which can
accommodate the largest vessels at any state of the tide,
and has excellent train services to the City, the Midlands,
and the north.

London deals with about one-third of the total foreign trade
of Britain. It handles about 40 per cent of our imports, but,
as it is not situated near the great manufacturing areas of
the Midlands and the north, it handles only about a quarter
of our exports. Among the imports the leading items are
frozen and chilled meat, grain and flour, wool, tea, sugar,
butter, and cheese. The leading exports are woollen goods,

cotton goods, clothing, metals, machinery, and miscellaneous manufactured goods.

The industries of London are characterized by their great variety, but the outstanding ones are the manufacture of clothing, boots and shoes, specialized metal goods, furniture, and paper.

Routes and Towns of the London Basin

All the trunk lines of the British Railways radiate from London like the spokes of a wheel from the hub.

The former L.N.E.R. has four main lines, viz.:

(1) From Liverpool Street Station to Harwich, Yarmouth, etc.

(2) From Liverpool Street Station to Cambridge and King's Lynn.

(3) From King's Cross northward to Peterborough, and thence through York and Newcastle into Scotland.

(4) From Marylebone Station, across the Chilterns by the dry gap between Chesham and Wendover, and thence through Rugby and Leicester to the north.

The former L.M. & S. main lines run from Euston and St Pancras Stations, the former crossing the Chilterns by the dry gap between Berkhampstead and Tring, and continuing north-ward through Northampton and Rugby, while the latter crosses the Chilterns by the water gap of the Lea at Luton, and con-tinues northward via Bedford and Leicester.

The former G.W.R. runs from Paddington, via the Thames valley to Reading, whence lines diverge to the Midlands, to Bristol and South Wales, and to the south-western peninsula.

The former S.R. runs from Waterloo, Victoria, and London Bridge Stations, to Plymouth, Southampton, and all the

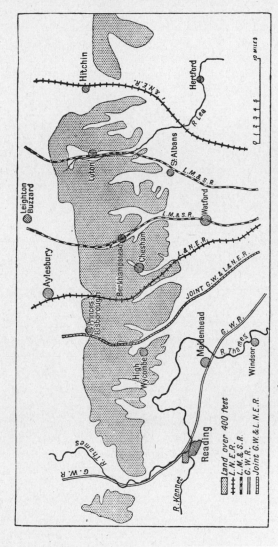

FIG. 68. THE WIND AND WATER GAPS IN THE CHILTERNS

(The initials indicate the ownership of the railways prior to nationalization)

chief ports and holiday resorts of the south coast, utilizing the dry gaps and river gaps in the North and South Downs (see Fig. 60).

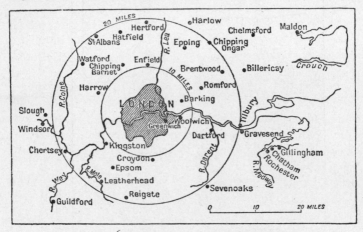

FIG. 69. LONDON AND ITS ENVIRONS
(Note the 10-mile and 20-mile circles)

Other towns of the London basin may be considered in relation to their manufacturing industries, which may be grouped as follows:

(1) Old-established industries which owe their origin to local supplies of raw material. *High Wycombe*, for example, has for long been famous as the centre of the chair-making industry. Originally the chairs were made by hand from the local beech wood, but nowadays the industry is carried on chiefly in factories, and a large part of the timber is imported. It will be seen that the industries of these towns form excellent examples of the principle of industrial inertia (see page 62). *Reading* has an old-established biscuit industry, which originally drew its supplies of flour from the locally grown wheat.

(2) Industries which still depend on local supplies of raw material. The chief of such industries is the manufacture of cement at Rochester and Gillingham, the materials used being chalk and mud dredged from the bed of the Medway.

(3) Modern industries which owe their origin to the supply of electrical power from the 'grid' system, the facilities for assembling raw materials, the proximity of the London market, the abundance of labour supply, and the comparatively low cost of land for factory sites. Most of these recently established industries specialize in products which are valuable in proportion to their bulk and to the amount of raw material which they contain, e.g. wireless sets, electrical apparatus, household utensils, prepared foods, etc. One of the most important of the new industrial centres in Greater London is *Slough*, two miles north-east of Windsor.

The manufacture of motor cars is carried on principally at Luton, Slough, and Dagenham, the Ford factory at the last-named centre being unique in that it makes its own steel from sea-borne iron ore.

EXAMINATION QUESTIONS

1. Describe and account for the distribution of population *either* in the Humber basin (excluding the Trent) *or* in the Thames basin. A sketch-map should accompany your answer. (L. M.)

2. Where are the chief chalk belts of England, and how do you account for their existence? (L. M.)

3. Examine the land approaches to London *either* on the north side *or* on the south side. Indicate the natural features which have rendered these approaches suitable for railway building, and point out the importance of the various railways. (L. M.)

4. With regard to London point out (*a*) what geographical factors decided its exact position on the Thames; (*b*) why it has become an industrial city; (*c*) the nature of its trade. (L. M.)

5. Describe *either* the London basin *or* the Fenlands under the headings: (*a*) relief and drainage; (*b*) climate; (*c*) occupations. Include a sketch-map of the region you select. (D. S. C.)

6. Draw a map of England and Wales, south of the Mersey-Humber line. On it mark areas which are important for (*a*) wheat; (*b*) fruit; (*c*) hops; (*d*) sheep. Explain why you choose the areas. (D. S. C.)

7. What do you understand by the London basin? Give a brief general account of the basin and of the geographical position of London. (L. G. S.)

8. What factors have influenced the concentration of railways on London? Illustrate your answer by a sketch-map. (D. M.)

9. The kind of farming practised in Britain is dependent on (*a*) relief and soils; (*b*) climate; (*c*) marketing facilities. Show how these factors have influenced agriculture in *three* of the following: the Cotswolds, the plain of Hereford, the lower Thames basin, the Cheshire plain.
(D. M.)

10. Illustrate by means of a diagram the structure and drainage of England south-east of the Cotswolds.
What are the chief areas in which industry is developing, apart from London, and why? (D. M.)

11. 'A line drawn from Grimsby on the Humber to Exeter on the Exe divides England and Wales into two widely different portions.'
Describe concisely the chief points of difference, arranging your answer under the headings: (*a*) relief; (*b*) agriculture; (*c*) minerals; (*d*) density of population. (C. S. C.)

12. Compare the physical features of North Wales with those of the scarp land south of the Thames. (O. S. C.)

13. On the railway lines between (*a*) London and Brighton and (*b*) London and Birmingham, where and why would you find (i) level stretches, (ii) tunnels or deep cuttings? Your answer must be illustrated by sketch-maps. (C. S. C.)

CHAPTER XV

SCOTLAND

STRUCTURE AND RELIEF

FIG. 4 shows that Scotland consists of five great blocks which are bounded by lines converging on a point in western Ireland. These blocks are:

(1) The *Southern Uplands*, which merge southwards into the Cheviot Hills, and are bounded on the north by the great fault which runs from Girvan to Dunbar. The Uplands are not a true range of hills, but the remnants of a great plateau which has been dissected by the weather and streams.

(2) The *Central Plain*, which is a great rift valley, formed by the land slipping down between the two faults which run from Girvan to Dunbar, and from Helensburgh, on the Firth of Clyde, to Stonehaven on the east coast.

(3) The *Grampian Highlands*, which lie between the northern boundary fault of the central plain and Glenmore, a deep trench which follows another series of faults. The Grampians, like the Southern Uplands, are the remnants of a dissected plateau, but the valleys are deeper, and the peaks are higher. Ben Nevis (4,406 feet) is the highest mountain of the British Isles, but the largest area of very high land is in the north-east, around Ben Macdhui (4,296 feet).

(4) The *Northern Highlands*, which lie to the north of Glenmore and are structurally similar to the Grampians,

though the mountains do not rise to such great heights. A remarkable feature of both the Grampians and the Northern Highlands is the large number of long, narrow, ribbon-like lakes which occupy hollows scooped out by glaciers along fault-lines. On the west coast these valleys are continued seawards by long, narrow lochs which are very similar to the fiords of Norway.

(5) The *Outer Hebrides*, which are separated from the mainland by the deep channel known as the Minch. This channel is really a submerged rift valley, since it was formed by the sinking of the land between faults which follow its shores. The islands which compose the Outer Hebrides represent the last remnants of a mountain range which has been worn down almost to sea-level.

CLIMATE

Since Scotland is much more mountainous than England it is on the whole much wetter and colder. The areas of heaviest rainfall are situated near the west coast, where the high mountains approach close to the sea. The rainfall gradually diminishes eastwards, the eastern coastal plains having only twenty-five to thirty inches per year— that is, about as much as the English Midlands. With regard to temperature, the most remarkable feature is the mildness of the winters. Contrary to the general belief, the *sea-level* temperatures for January are approximately the same as those of England. Cape Wrath, in the extreme north-west corner of Scotland, has about the same January average as Brighton, and Aberdeen is practically as warm as London. (See the January isotherm map, Fig. 11, and the discussion of the temperature of the British Isles on page 16.) In summer the temperature decreases northward, and the lowest *actual* temperatures of the British Isles are experienced on the mountains of the Grampians, while the lowest sea-level temperatures are found in the Orkneys and the Shetlands.

THE SOUTHERN UPLANDS

I. FARMING

This region shows very clearly the relationship between relief and climate on the one hand and the type of farming on the other. *Cattle-rearing* is most important in the mild, moist lowlands of Ayrshire, Wigtown, and Kirkcudbright, which specialize in the production of milk for sale in the towns of the central plain. Few cattle are reared in the mountainous counties of Peebles and Selkirk, but on the lowlands of the Tweed basin many beef cattle are raised, though the total number of cattle per square mile in Berwick is less than half of the number in Wigtown.

Sheep are most numerous in the mountainous districts of the centre and in the rain-shadow area of the Tweed basin. Here three types of sheep land may be recognized, viz.:

(1) Heather moors, where each sheep needs two to four acres of land, and the farms are consequently very large. On such upland pastures the chief type of sheep is the hardy black-faced variety.

(2) The grasslands of the lower hill-slopes, where the farms are smaller, and the less hardy, white-faced Cheviot sheep is dominant.

(3) The lowlands, where the sheep are kept as part of the system of mixed farming as in Lincolnshire (see page 93). Here the sheep are generally cross-breeds, the hardy Black-face and Cheviot being crossed with English varieties.

Arable Farming. As in England, a much greater proportion

of the farm land is under plough on the drier eastern side of the country than in the wetter west. Berwick has, in proportion to its area, two and a half times as much arable land as Ayrshire, and five times as much as the mountainous county of Peebles. Wheat is hardly grown at all in the west and central districts, while even in Berwick only 5 per cent of the arable land is devoted to its cultivation. Barley is likewise confined to the eastern coastlands from Berwick to the Moray Firth. Most of the crop is of the high quality used for brewing. Oats, which thrive under varying climatic conditions, are more widely distributed than other cereals, and the lowlands of the extreme south-west produce almost as much as those of the Tweed basin. The yield of grain is, however, much greater in the east than in the west. Early potatoes are a great speciality of the coastlands of Ayrshire, and seed potatoes of the eastern coastal plain as far north as Aberdeen.

II. THE WOOLLEN INDUSTRY OF THE TWEED BASIN

In the early days of the Industrial Revolution the Tweed basin possessed all the factors necessary for the development of woollen manufacturing, viz.: local supplies of wool, soft water for washing the wool, rapid streams for water-power, and inhabitants skilled in the processes of spinning and weaving. With the advent of steam-power, however, the industry was handicapped by the lack of local coal, but it has survived by specialization in products of high quality (cf. the west of England district, page 116). The characteristic product of the region is the suitings known as 'tweeds,' the patterns of which were originally based on those which had long been used for shepherds' plaids. The cloth itself was originally known as 'tweel,' but this name is said to have been changed to 'tweeds' by an English clerk, who apparently thought that the cloth should be named after the district where it was manufactured.

The chief centres for the manufacture of tweeds are Galashiels and Selkirk. Hawick specializes in the manufacture of knitwear made from wool, mohair, and artificial fibres.

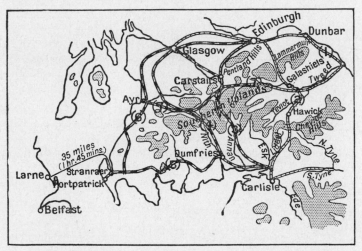

FIG. 70. SOUTH SCOTLAND—PHYSICAL AND RAILWAYS

III. THE RAILWAYS

Southern Scotland is, on the whole, one of the most thinly peopled parts of Britain, but it is, nevertheless, served by many main lines of railway, which link the densely peopled central plain to northern England and London. Fortunately, there are several river valleys which have facilitated the construction of north-to-south railways, and there are few districts which show so clearly the control exercised by relief upon the lines of communication. Four main lines from

England to the central plain of Scotland should be traced, viz.:

(1) The 'East Coast' route, which follows the eastern coastal plain from Berwick, through Dunbar, to Edinburgh. This is, of course, a continuation of the main line from London, through York and Newcastle.

(2) The 'Waverley' route, which runs from Carlisle to Edinburgh, following the valleys of the Liddel (a tributary of the Esk), and the Teviot and the Gala (tributaries of the Tweed). The route gets its name from the fact that it passes through the district in which Sir Walter Scott lived when he wrote the Waverley Novels.

(3) The 'Caledonian' route, which runs up the valley of the Annan, and down the upper Clyde valley to Carstairs Junction, whence one line runs via the Clyde valley to Glasgow, and another runs round the western end of the Pentland Hills to Edinburgh.

(4) The 'South-western' route, which runs via Dumfries and Nithsdale to Kilmarnock, and thence to Glasgow.

Other important routes are:

(5) The line along the south coast to Portpatrick and the packet station of Stranraer, whence steamers ply to Larne in Northern Ireland.

(6) The line along the west coast through Girvan and Ayr and on to Paisley and Glasgow.

(7) The east to west route from Berwick to Ayr via the valleys of the Tweed and the Ayr.

The Central Plain

Though this area comprises only about 10 per cent of the area of Scotland, it contains about 80 per cent of the population. The reasons for this high density of population are:

(1) It is the largest area of fertile lowland.

(2) It is one of the chief coal-mining areas in Britain.

(3) Deposits of iron are found in close proximity to the coal, and these, though little worked at present, gave rise to the iron and steel industries.

(4) The navigable estuaries provide shelter for ocean steamers and enable them to penetrate far into the land, thus facilitating foreign trade.

(5) The level land has facilitated the construction of roads, canals, and railways.

Most of the characteristic features of the central plain can be shown to be the result of the sinking of the land which formed the rift valley. Its fertility is due partly to the preservation of softer rocks which have been worn away from the neighbouring highlands, and partly to the deposition of sediment washed down from those highlands by the rivers. The deep estuaries or firths of the Clyde, the Forth, and the Tay are due to the 'drowning' of the lower courses of the rivers as a consequence of the sinking of the land. The folding of the rocks, which accompanied the sinking of the crust, caused the separation of the coal-measures into a number of basins, in which the coal-seams have been preserved, while they have been worn away from the intervening up-folds. The ranges—Lennox Hills, Ochil Hills, and Sidlaw Hills—which form the southern boundary of the broad Vale of Strathmore, represent one such upfold which has been dissected by the Rivers Clyde, Forth, and Tay. Again, the formation of the rift valley was undoubtedly accompanied by great volcanic activity, molten rock being forced out at the surface by the sinking crust blocks. The hard cores or 'plugs' of such ancient volcanoes still remain in many parts of the central valley, and some of them are crowned with castles.

FARMING IN THE CENTRAL PLAIN

In spite of the narrowness of the central plain, the eastern and western sides show the same contrasts as were noted in England and in southern Scotland. Thus the wetter, western half has a larger percentage of permanent grassland and many more dairy cattle than the drier east, while barley, sugar-beet, and wheat are practically confined to the eastern districts. The county of Fife, for example, has, in proportion to its area, twice as much arable land, and nearly four times as much wheat land as Renfrew. The following districts in the eastern half of the central plain are specially notable for their productivity:

(1) The eastern half of Strathmore, between the Sidlaw Hills and the Highland boundary fault. A distinctive feature of this region is the cultivation of raspberries around Blairgowrie in Perthshire.

(2) The Carse of Gowrie, a fertile lowland situated between the Sidlaw Hills and the estuary of the Tay. Most of the farmers specialize in the production of cereals, beans, and seed potatoes, and certain parishes are famous for the production of raspberries and strawberries.

(3) The Lothian Lowland, which includes those parts of the counties of Linlithgow (West Lothian), Edinburgh (Midlothian), and Haddington (East Lothian) which are below the 500-foot contour-line. These lowlands comprise the best farm lands in Scotland and specialize in the production of wheat, barley, potatoes, and root crops.

THE SCOTTISH COAL-FIELDS

The five coal-fields of Scotland are:

(1) The Ayrshire coal-field.

(2) The Lanarkshire or Central coal-field.

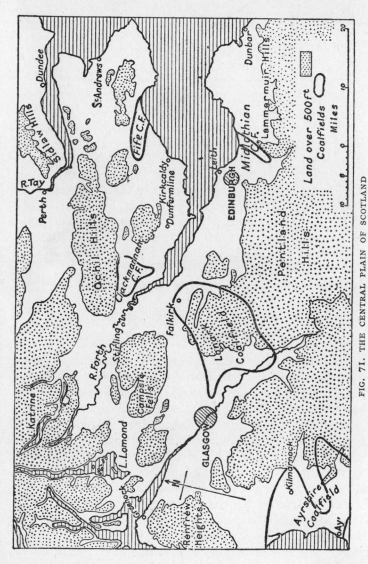

FIG. 71. THE CENTRAL PLAIN OF SCOTLAND

(3) The Clackmannan coal-field.

(4) The Fife coal-field.

(5) The Midlothian coal-field.

These fields together produce about 10 per cent of the total British output. Lanarkshire produces about half the Scottish output, Fifeshire about a quarter, and Midlothian and Ayrshire nearly one-eighth each. Mining is generally more difficult than in England, and though some high-class coal is produced, the quality is on the whole poorer than that of English coal. Most of the coal produced in the western half of the central plain is used in that district, but about a third of the coal produced in the eastern districts is shipped as bunker coal. The chief coal ports are Leith, Methil, Granton, Bo'ness, and Grangemouth. The last-named port is also important for oil refining and 'cracking.'

Oil shale, from which ammonia, motor-spirit, and lamp-oil are distilled, is mined on the eastern fringe of the Lanark coal-field, and in West Lothian and Midlothian.

THE IRON AND STEEL INDUSTRIES

The Lanarkshire coal-field formerly possessed two great advantages for the production of iron and steel, viz.: 'blackband' iron ore, which required little additional fuel for smelting, and hard 'splint' coal, which was suitable for use in the furnaces without preliminary coking. In modern times local supplies of both ore and 'splint' coal have become almost exhausted, but the iron and steel industries have survived on the basis of imported ore, pig iron, and semi-finished steel. The chief centres of the industries are: *Falkirk*, which imports most of its raw material via Grangemouth; a group of towns in the Clyde valley—*Coatbridge*, *Airdrie*, *Motherwell*, and *Wishaw*; and *Irvine* in Ayrshire.

The *shipbuilding industry* consumes a large proportion of

the steel produced in Scotland, the chief centres being Clyde-bank, Dumbarton, Port Glasgow, and Greenock, all of which are situated on the estuary of the Clyde. This region is the most important shipbuilding district in the world, and in normal years produces about a third of the tonnage of shipping

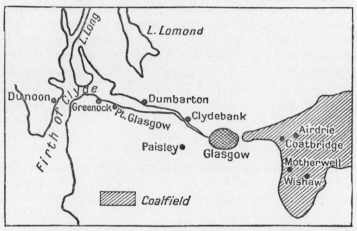

FIG. 72. IRON-WORKING AND SHIPBUILDING TOWNS OF THE CLYDE VALLEY

launched in Great Britain. The reasons for the growth of the shipbuilding industry on the estuary of the Clyde are:

(1) The sheltered, navigable waterway.

(2) The nearby supplies of iron and coal, and the facilities for importing pig-iron, steel, and other materials.

(3) The fact that one of the first successful steamships, the *Comet*, was built and launched there (1812).

Engineering is the chief industry of the western half of the central plain. The chief specialities are marine engineering, locomotive-building, boiler-making, and the manufacture of machine tools.

THE TEXTILE INDUSTRIES

Cotton. Glasgow and the surrounding district possesses the same advantage as Lancashire for the manufacture of cotton goods, viz.: numerous rapid streams, abundance of coal and iron, a humid climate, a dense population, and a convenient port for the importation of raw cotton. The area was indeed a serious rival of Lancashire in the early part of the nineteenth century, but its greater suitability for the iron and steel industries caused these to grow at the expense of cotton manufacturing. Two branches of the industry which have survived are the manufacture of cotton thread at Paisley, and of curtain net at Glasgow.

Linen manufacturing was formerly carried on as a domestic industry throughout the central lowlands. It has, however, continued as a factory industry only in the eastern districts, where conditions are not so suitable for the manufacture of cotton goods. Towns which still manufacture some quantity of linen goods are Dundee, Kirkcaldy, and Dunfermline.

Jute, which is used for the manufacture of canvas and sacking, is the coarse fibre obtained from the inner bark of a plant which is cultivated chiefly in the Ganges delta. Early in the nineteenth century the linen manufacturers of Dundee began to experiment in the use of jute fibre, and when supplies of Russian flax were cut off during the Crimean War the jute industry quickly expanded at the expense of linen. Dundee now manufactures about one-seventh of the world's jute cloth, but the industry suffers from the severe competition of the factories in Calcutta, which have the double advantage of nearness to the supplies of raw material and abundance of very cheap labour.

MISCELLANEOUS INDUSTRIES

Linoleum is manufactured chiefly in Kirkcaldy, which is specially noted for the high quality of its products. The industry may be regarded as an outgrowth from the jute industry of Dundee, which supplies the canvas backing used as the base. Other raw materials are cork, which comes chiefly from Spain, and linseed oil, some of which is produced locally from imported linseed. A subsidiary industry is the manufacture of cattle cake from the residue of the oil seeds.

Sugar refining is carried on chiefly at Greenock, where the industry developed as the result of Glasgow's early trade connection with the West Indies.

Jam is made at Dundee and Paisley, both of which are conveniently situated near fruit-growing areas. The marmalade industry of Dundee is said to owe its origin, in part, to the ease with which oranges could be imported from Spain as deck cargo on ships bringing jute from India.

CITIES AND RAILWAY ROUTES

Glasgow is the largest city of Scotland and the fifth port of the British Isles in respect of the value of its foreign trade. It grew up at the lowest bridge-point on the Clyde, and is the natural focus of land routes in the western half of the central plain. As a port, however, it owes more to the work of man than to the gifts of nature. A century ago the river was fordable at Glasgow at low tide, and was unnavigable at high tide by vessels drawing more than seven feet of water. Port Glasgow, situated twelve miles downstream, served the city until, in the nineteenth century, the channel was deepened by dredging and by blasting away huge masses of rock, thus providing a waterway into the heart of the city capable of accommodating at low tide vessels drawing twenty-five feet of water. As a port, Glasgow is characterized by the high value of its exports, which normally exceed the imports by 60 per cent. The reasons for this difference are: (a) Glasgow serves primarily the manufacturing district of south-western Scotland, which depends chiefly on overseas markets for the disposal of its products; (b) a very large proportion of the foodstuffs consumed by the industrial population is imported via Leith and other eastern ports.

Edinburgh grew up around the castle which, built on an old volcanic plug, dominates the coastal route from England to the Scottish Lowlands. As the former political capital and the present educational and cultural capital of Scotland, its growth has kept pace with the increasing prosperity of the country as a whole. Its industries—printing, the preparation of foodstuffs, and the manufacture of paper and scientific instruments—are those characteristic of capital cities. *Leith*, which is now a part of Edinburgh, is the chief port of eastern Scotland. Its chief imports are dairy produce, esparto grass and wood pulp for paper-making, grain for the brewing industry of Edinburgh, and pit-props for the Scottish coal-fields. *Granton*, situated three miles to the west of Leith, is another port which is now included within the city boundaries. It is a fishing centre, and specializes in the importation of timber and other bulky products.

Stirling and *Perth* have many characteristics in common. Each is situated at the lowest bridge-point of its river and at the head of navigation of its estuary; each is at the natural focus of land routes from the Highlands, Strathmore, and the central plain; and each has played a great part in the history of the country. Perth was the capital of Scotland until the assassination of James I in 1437, and near by is the former royal palace of Scone, from which the coronation stone was taken to Westminster Abbey. In modern times Perth, favoured by the special suitability of the waters of the Tay, has developed a great dyeing industry. Stirling grew up round a castle which, like that of Edinburgh, crowns an ancient volcanic plug. It is an important railway junction, and, as it is situated on the edge of the central coal-field, it has developed industries such as the manufacture of carpets and tweeds.

Dundee, which controls the coastal route to north-eastern Scotland, is situated at the point where the Tay estuary narrows before again opening out to the sea. It first rose to importance as a whaling station, and though this industry is now dead, the port is one of the chief fishing ports of the British Isles. The proximity of Dundee to the Fifeshire coal-field aided the development of the jute, linen, and jam-making industries, and the building of the Tay Bridge gave it additional importance as a railway centre.

St Andrews, situated on the coast of the lowland known as the Howe of Fife, is famous for its golf-courses and for its university, which is the oldest in Scotland.

The *railway routes* of central Scotland show, in contrast to those of the Southern Uplands, a marked east to west alignment. Three main lines, with numerous interconnections, run from Edinburgh to Glasgow, while farther north the lines show a marked parallelism with the upfold separating Strathmore from the rest of the central valley. There are also four main lines running northwards to the Highland region:

(1) From Edinburgh, via the Forth Bridge or round by Stirling, to Perth, and thence by the Tay and Spey valleys to Inverness.

(2) From Edinburgh, via the Forth Bridge and the Tay Bridge to Dundee and thence along the east coast.

(3) From Edinburgh, via Stirling and Callander to the west coast.

(4) From Glasgow, via Dumbarton to the west coast.

Edinburgh and Glasgow are linked by a canal which utilizes the gap in the hills west of Falkirk. Unfortunately, the canal can accommodate only small barges, and proposals for the construction of a ship canal following roughly the same course have been turned down on account of the high cost of construction.

The Highlands and North-eastern Scotland

The Scottish Highlands are one of the most thinly populated regions in Europe, the average density being less than ten per square mile, while there are vast areas which are entirely lacking in human settlements. The reasons for the sparseness of the population are:

(1) The mountainous character of the land.

(2) The existence of a large number of valley lakes, which greatly reduce the area of cultivable lowland.

(3) The hardness of the rock, which causes the soil to be thin and infertile.

(4) The lack of limestone to counteract the natural acidity of the soil.

(5) The moist climate, which is unfavourable for agriculture.

(6) The lack of minerals, which has prevented the development of manufacturing industries.

(7) The difficulty of communication, which has hindered the development of the fishing industry.

The climatic conditions do not favour the growth of forest or meadow grass, and the mountains are covered with heather,

Topical Press

Edinburgh—Princes Street

Will F. Taylor

Crofters' Cottages, Old and New

bracken, and coarse brown grass. Some of the rough mountain pastures are utilized as sheep-runs, but the herbage is so
poor that the farms are very large, and the low, stone-built
cottages of the shepherds are very widely separated. In
recent years large areas have been reserved as privately
owned grouse moors and deer 'forests' which produce practically nothing of economic value. Arable farming is, of
course, confined to small alluvial flats which occur at the
bottoms of some of the deep glens. The chief 'money' crop
of such valley farms is young cattle, which are sold to the
Lowland farmers for fattening. Throughout the Highlands
the proportion of cattle to arable land is very high, though
the number of cattle per square mile is very low indeed.

The *Crofters*. In the western Highlands and in the Northern
and Western Isles (the Orkneys, the Shetlands, and the Hebrides) the farms are known as 'crofts,' and the farmers and
their families as 'crofters.' Each family has a small patch
of arable land on which oats, potatoes, and hay are grown,
as well as a large area of poor mountain pasture which provides summer feed for the sheep. In summer the men spend
much of their time fishing, in order to supplement the foodstuffs produced on the farm. Even so, most of the crofters have
to depend for the major portion of their income on the weaving
of the 'Harris' tweeds, so greatly prized for their warmth,
durability, and special colouring. Formerly the cloth was
manufactured entirely in the homes from local materials only.
Now most of the wool is brought from the mainland and spun
and dyed in mills situated in Stornaway. The dyed yarn is
distributed to the crofters, who weave it in their outhouses, or
in the old, rough-stone, single-storey buildings which were
formerly the typical houses of the islands.

After weaving, the cloth is sent back to the mills for finishing
and marketing. In a typical year over a million pounds'

* G

worth of cloth is sent from the islands, about half of it to the United States. In the Shetlands the women earn a little money by the sale of their hand-knit shawls, etc., made from the fine, soft wool of the local breed of sheep.

North-eastern Scotland differs markedly from the true Highland region. It is built chiefly of comparatively soft Old Red Sandstone which has been worn down to form fairly extensive and fertile lowlands, the climate is drier and sunnier than that of the west, and there is consequently far more cultivated land on the eastern than on the western side. The chief agricultural areas are the north-eastern shoulder of Aberdeenshire and the lowlands around the Moray Firth. The chief crop is oats, the amount of land devoted to this cereal exceeding that in any other part of Scotland. Turnips and swedes are also of great importance in both areas, and Aberdeenshire is specially noted for its beef cattle. Some barley is grown on the coastal plain, but the only area which is dry enough for wheat is the coastal fringe of the Moray Firth.

ROUTES AND TOWNS IN NORTHERN SCOTLAND

Four lines of railway run into the Highland region from the central plain. They are:

(1) The east-coast route from Dundee to Aberdeen, where the line cuts across the north-eastern shoulder to Elgin and Inverness.

(2) The Highland route from Perth, via the valleys of the Tay, the Tummel, the Garry, the upper Spey (see Fig. 73). From Inverness routes continue northwards via the eastern coastal plain to the fishing ports of Thurso and Wick, and

westward to Strome Ferry and the Kyle of Lochalsh on the west coast.

(3) From Stirling, through Callander to Oban on the west coast.

(4) From Glasgow, through Dumbarton and thence through Fort William to Mallaig on the west coast.

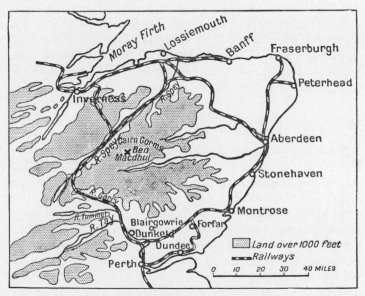

FIG. 73. NORTH-EASTERN SCOTLAND

The *Caledonian Canal* connects the lochs which lie in the great trough of Glenmore. At the time of its construction, more than a century ago, it was expected that it would be much used by vessels plying from Glasgow to North Sea ports. It is, however, too small for modern cargo vessels, and is used only by fishing vessels and tourist steamers. *Inverness*, at the northern end, is an important route centre and was the key to the military control of northern Scotland during the Hanoverian period. *Fort William* at the southern end is a small settlement which grew up around another fortress built in the same period.

Aberdeen first grew up at the mouth of the Dee, but now occupies nearly all the area between the estuaries of the Dee and the Don. It is an important fishing station, and the chief commercial port of northern Scotland. Its chief industries are the building of steel trawlers, and the manufacture of paper. The chief export is dried and salted fish, which is sent to the Baltic countries. Granite, which is quarried in the vicinity, is also exported.

WATER-POWER IN SCOTLAND

Great Britain, in comparison with countries such as Norway, Sweden, Switzerland, and Canada, is not very well suited for the development of hydro-electricity, since our mountainous areas are in general too small to provide a great and constant volume of water. The Highlands of Scotland, because of their great extent, fairly great height, and abundant rainfall, and numerous lakes which act as natural storage reservoirs, are obviously the most suitable district in Britain for the hydro-electrical development, and several stations near the line of Glenmore are now in operation. The chief of these are: *Loch Foyers*, on the eastern side of Glenmore; *Kinlochleven*, on a tributary loch on the eastern side of Loch Linnhe; *Fort William*, which derives some of its power from water led from Loch Laggan by a fifteen-mile tunnel through a shoulder of Ben Nevis; and *Loch Rannoch*, at the upper end of the Tummel, a tributary of the Tay. This last-named scheme produces electricity to supplement that generated by steam-power in the central lowlands, while the first three installations provide power for the electrical smelting of aluminium. Over a hundred new hydro-electric stations have been planned in the Highlands, the largest projects being those of the Tay basin and Loch Sloy (west of Loch Lomond).

In southern Scotland the chief hydro-electric stations are situated at the Falls of the Clyde, and near Kirkcudbright in the south-west.

EXAMINATION QUESTIONS

1. Study the map (Fig. 74) showing the distribution of population by counties in Scotland. (a) Name *one* area of dense, *one* of sparse

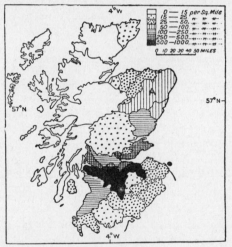

FIG. 74. POPULATION MAP OF SCOTLAND BY COUNTIES

population. (b) Explain how in each of the two areas named in (a) the particular density or sparsity is affected by relief, climate, and character of occupations. (c) (i) What information can you obtain from the map about the distribution of population in Aberdeenshire (marked A on the map)? (ii) State any facts you can about the distribution of population in Aberdeenshire *other than those shown by the map*. (N. U.)

2. State the principal industries carried on in the manufacturing district round Glasgow, and name the towns noted for each industry. Show on a sketch-map the towns which you name. (O. S. C.)

3. Describe the chief physical conditions which control the distribution of population in the Highlands of Scotland. Which parts are most densely populated? Show in what ways these parts differ from the rest of the Highlands. (O. S. C.)

4. Of the three counties, Aberdeen, Cheshire, Norfolk, which has the greatest *percentage* of: (*a*) mountain and heath; (*b*) arable land; (*c*) meadow-land? In relation to these facts discuss briefly the type of farming carried on in each of the three counties. (N. U.)

5. Describe *two* railway routes *either* from the north of England into the Lowlands of Scotland *or* from the midlands of England to the west coast of Wales. Indicate the commercial importance of *one* of these routes. (N. U.)

6. Give a reasoned account of the distribution and density of population in (*a*) the north-west Highlands of Scotland, and (*b*) Norfolk and Suffolk. (N. U.)

7. Give geographical reasons accounting for the fact that hydro-electric power is more developed in Switzerland than in the British Isles. Locate *two* examples in the British Isles of the utilization of water-power on a commercial scale and describe the industrial uses to which the power is put. (N. U.)

8. Compare the physical and climatic features of (*a*) south Lancashire and Cheshire with those of (*b*) the lands bordering the Firth of Forth, and show how these features have affected the chief farming activities in *each* area. (C. S. C.)

9. Describe the geographical factors which have helped to make the lower valleys of the Clyde and the Tyne the most important ship-building areas in the British Isles. (C. S. C.)

10. Describe systematically the south of Scotland (the area between the great central or rift valley and the Border), from the point of view of relief and drainage, and of the distribution of rainfall, temperature, and agricultural products. (L. M.)

11. Draw a sketch-map to show the areas of greatest density of population in *either* Scotland *or* Wales. Give full reasons for the density in the areas you mark. (D. S. C.)

12. Describe the distribution of textile industries in Scotland, and the geographical conditions which favour each. (D. M.)

13. Contrast the outstanding characteristics of the relief and topography of the following areas, giving what you consider the more important reasons for the differences: (a) the Grampians, and (b) the Pennines. (W. M.)

14. In what parts of Scotland is tweed cloth produced, and what factors account for the production? (C. S. C.)

15. Draw a sketch-map to show the relief and drainage of *either* the Thames basin *or* the Clyde basin. The map should show also the distribution of the human activities within the basin selected.
(L. M.)

16. 'Scotland is a land of contrasts.' Give reasons which appear to justify the use of this expression. (L. M.)

17. Show how the East Coast route from London to Edinburgh is related to the relief of the land. (L. M.)

18. Compare, and contrast, the central Highlands of Scotland and the peninsula of Devon and Cornwall with regard to (a) physical features; (b) climate; (c) agriculture. (L. G. S.)

19. The railway routes from north England to the central Lowlands of Scotland are controlled by the physical character of the area between. Name the major routes of the railways and show how they are controlled by the relief conditions. Illustrate your answer with a sketch-map. (D. M.)

20. Discuss the trade at the ports on the Firths of Tay and Forth.
(L. G. S.)

21. Write a geographical account of *either* the Severn basin *or* the Clyde basin, under the headings: (a) position and extent; (b) relief and drainage; (c) climate; (d) occupations, towns, and communications. (D. M.)

22. What exactly is meant by 'climate'? Illustrate your answer by describing the conditions on the east and the west coast of Scotland. (O. S. C.)

23. Name, and describe the position of, *one* great sea-fishing port in England, and *one* in Scotland, and discuss the chief shore occupations of those ports depending on the fishing.

What special advantages has Great Britain for this industry?
(C. S. C.)

24. Select one English and one Scottish manufacturing industry. In each case name one locality, and discuss the important factors which have helped to determine this location.   (C. S. C.)

25. Draw a large sketch-map of the southern uplands of Scotland. Indicate and name on the map *three* important river valleys.

Explain (*a*) why the river valleys are important; (*b*) why the occupations in the eastern half differ from those in the western half of the region.   (C. S. C.)

26. Comment on and explain the following statements concerning the 1931 census:

(*a*) 'The population of Scotland shows a decrease for the first time since the first census was taken in 1801. Lanarkshire has 32·8 per cent of the total population of the country; 69·4 per cent of the population live in towns, and decreases are recorded in 27 out of the 33 counties.'

(*b*) 'The outstanding features of the recent census of England are the southward trend of the population and the increase in the population in the south-east.'   (O. S. C.)

27. Write an account of the textile industries in the Midland Valley of Scotland, showing their position, the sources of the raw materials, and the local geographical conditions that have affected their development.   (O. S. C.)

28. Describe the differences between the climate and agriculture of East Anglia and of western Scotland, north of the Clyde, and show how in each case the type of agriculture is related to climatic conditions.   (O. S. C.)

29. Write a concise account of the chief factors which influence the distribution of rainfall in Scotland.   (C. S. C.)

CHAPTER XVI

IRELAND

IRELAND is often described as a saucer-shaped island, since most of the high land is situated around the edges. The simile is, however, not very apt, since the 'rim' of high land consists of detached fragments, many of which extend well inland, while the central lowland extends to the coast in several places. We have already seen that Ireland consists of detached fragments of Great Britain, and the structure lines shown on Fig. 4 form the approximate boundaries of the following natural divisions:

(1) North-western Ireland, which includes the barren mountainous regions of Tirconnail (Donegal), Mayo, and Connemara.

(2) North-eastern Ireland, which includes the mountains of Mourne and the plateau of Antrim. The latter is built up of volcanic rock formed by the cooling of lava which in comparatively recent geological times welled up from great cracks in the earth. That these lava-flows formerly extended across what is now the North Channel is shown by the existence of similar volcanic rock in the islands of Staffa and Iona, near the mainland of Scotland. When the lava cooled, the contraction caused the rock to split up into columns such as those which compose Giant's Causeway, and Fingal's Cave in the island of Staffa.

(3) South-eastern Ireland, which includes the mountains of Wicklow and the uplands of Wexford.

(4) South-western Ireland, which consists of alternating

ridges and valleys running roughly east and west. The ridges, which are continued out to sea as long promontories, are formed chiefly of hard Old Red Sandstone, while the intervening valleys, which are drowned at their seaward ends, are formed of limestone. The Macgillicuddy's Reeks contain the highest mountain in Ireland, and the district of Killarney is claimed to be the most picturesque in the country.

(5) The Central Plain, which extends to the east coast between Dundalk and Dublin, widens out westwards, and sends offshoots to the west coast around the mouth of the Shannon, Galway Bay, Clew Bay, and Donegal Bay.

The central plain is floored with carboniferous limestone, similar to that which makes up the northern Pennines, but as it is very low-lying and is in most places covered with glacial drift, it is waterlogged and swampy. Extensive bogs occupy hollows which have been formed by the solution of the underlying limestone, but the major portion of the plain consists of rather wet pasture land. Numerous sandy ridges, which are known as eskers, and which are thought to have been formed by the deposition of sediment by streams which flowed under the ice sheet, run across the plain. Their general direction is from east to west and many of them are followed by the main roads.

CLIMATE, ETC.

The outstanding features of the climate of Ireland are its humidity and its equability. The heaviest rainfall is, of course, experienced in the mountainous regions near the west coast, but these areas are not so wet as corresponding regions in Great Britain since the mountains do not rise much above the 3,000-foot line. The rain-shadow area to the east of the mountains is also not so strongly marked as in England, and the district around Dublin, which is the driest area in Ireland, has a rainfall of 25 to 30 inches and is, therefore, comparable with the Midland Plain of England.

The exceptional mildness of the Irish winters is due, like the heavy rainfall, to the fact that the country is fully exposed to the south-westerly winds. South-western Ireland has the highest winter temperatures of any part of the British Isles, and the average January temperature of Valentia Island is six degrees higher than that of London. In summer the island is on the whole cooler than that part of Great Britain which lies between the same lines of latitude.

The heavy rainfall and the mildness of the winters encourage the growth of grass, which gives to the landscape the predominant green colour which has earned for Ireland the name of the Emerald Isle.

Politically, Ireland is now divided into two countries: Northern Ireland, which is still a part of the United Kingdom and sends members to Westminster, though it has a Parliament of its own which sits at Belfast, and the Irish Republic, which is now a completely independent country.

Northern Ireland

The six counties which compose Northern Ireland constitute the major portion of the ancient province of Ulster. The inhabitants differ from those of the rest of Ireland in being mainly of Scottish or English descent, and in being mainly Protestants. For many centuries there was friction between them and the Catholic communities of the rest of Ireland, and in 1921, when the Irish Free State was granted Home Rule, Northern Ireland decided to remain part of the United Kingdom.

PHYSICAL FEATURES

The relief of Northern Ireland may be considered under the headings of :

(1) The marginal lowlands.
(2) The marginal highlands.
(3) The central lake basin surrounding Lough Neagh.

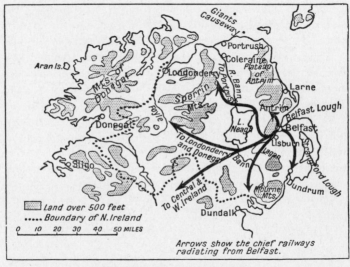

FIG. 75. NORTHERN IRELAND

(1) The *Marginal Lowlands* include the valley of the River Foyle and the southern shores of the estuary; the coastal plain around the mouth of the River Bann; the broad coastal plain of County Down, south of Belfast Lough; and the lake-studded lowland of Fermanagh, where the River Erne expands into scores of lakes which are known collectively as Upper and Lower Lough Erne.

(2) The *Marginal Highlands* include:

(*a*) The Sperrin Mountains, which rise to a height of 2,248 feet, and are composed of ancient crystalline rocks similar to those of the Scottish Highlands, of which they are indeed a detached portion (see Fig. 4).

(*b*) The Antrim plateau, which is composed of sheets of volcanic rock which almost completely conceal the underlying beds of chalk. The former extension of the lava-flows across the North Channel to the islands of the Inner Hebrides has already been mentioned (see page 193).

(*c*) The Mourne Mountains, which rise in Slieve Donard to 2,804 feet, and are composed of granite and other hard rocks similar to those of the southern uplands.

(3) The *Lough Neagh Basin* was formed by the subsidence of the land subsequent to the great outpourings of lava which built up the Antrim plateau. Lough Neagh itself has an area of 153 square miles, and is the largest lake in the British Isles. The surrounding plain is built up chiefly of glacial deposits and of sediments washed down from the surrounding highlands. It is on the whole a fertile farming region, but some parts of it are so level as to be waterlogged and suitable only for cattle pastures.

From the lake plain several corridors of lowland lead to the coast and to the Irish Free State. The chief of these are: the valley of the Bann, leading to the north coast; the Lagan valley, leading to Belfast Lough; the narrow gateway round the western end of the Mourne Mountains to Carlingford Lough; and the broad gateway leading south-westward through County Monaghan.

FARMING

Although Northern Ireland suffers from the disadvantages of cool weather, persistent rainfall, and a large proportion of high land, arable farming is of considerable importance, and though only a sixth of the land is arable, Northern Ireland is now one of the most highly mechanized farming areas in the United Kingdom. The country is predominantly a land of small farmers, two-thirds of the farms being less than thirty acres in size. The difficulties which usually beset the small farmer have, however, been largely overcome by the establishment of agricultural credit societies, and co-operative dairies and bacon factories.

Wheat will not ripen with certainty except in the driest parts of County Down, and even there only small quantities are grown. Oats are therefore the principal cereal, most of the crop being used for feeding to the farm animals, though considerable quantities are made into breakfast oats and oatmeal. Potatoes are the next most important crop, occupying about half the acreage given to oats. Most of the output is consumed within the country, but in normal years there is usually a surplus for export to England. Flax, from the fibres of which linen is prepared, was formerly the most important 'money' crop of Northern Ireland, but very little is now grown there, since the crop is difficult to harvest, tends to exhaust the fertility of the soil, and cannot be produced as cheaply as fibre imported from eastern Europe.

The chief aim of the Irish farmer is, however, the rearing of farm stock; cattle are reared for both beef and milk, the store cattle being largely exported to England, while the milk is sent to co-operative creameries, where it is made into butter which is likewise sent chiefly to England. As in Denmark, the rearing of pigs is closely associated with the dairying industry, since the separated milk forms excellent pig food. The bacon is cured at well-equipped central factories, and finds a ready market in England. Sheep are naturally not so numerous as in the drier parts of Great Britain, but considerable numbers are reared on the mountain pastures, on the moorlands of the Antrim plateau, and in those small areas where the wearing away of the volcanic rock has laid bare the underlying chalk. The most important item in the agricultural output of Northern Ireland is, however, the production of eggs and poultry. The importance of the industry may be gathered from the fact that Northern Ireland has almost as many head of poultry as the whole of Great Britain, while the annual value of the output is about equal to the value of milk and butter produced in Northern Ireland.

MINING

Northern Ireland is very poor in minerals. Coal-measures, which are a continuation of those occurring in the rift valley of Scotland, exist under the lava-flows of Antrim and crop out to the north-east of Lough Neagh. The seams are, however, thin and poor, and the output of coal is almost negligible. Bauxite, the mineral from which aluminium and alum are manufactured, is mined in Antrim and treated at Larne. Small quantities of iron ore were also formerly mined in the same district, but the output has now entirely ceased.

MANUFACTURING

In spite of the lack of coal and other minerals, Northern Ireland has become an important manufacturing region. The reasons which have given rise to the development of manufacturing industries are:

(1) The skill and enterprise of the inhabitants.

(2) The proximity to the coal- and iron-fields of western Scotland and north-western England.

(3) The facilities for the importation of raw materials and the export of finished products provided by the great port of Belfast.

The *Linen Industry*. Northern Ireland is the world's chief centre for the manufacture of linen, and provides, in fact, nearly one-third of the world's output. The reasons for the development of the industry may be summarized as follows:

(1) In the early days of the industry the cultivation of flax was encouraged by the occurrence of well-drained clay soils, by the moist climate, and by the system of smallholdings.

(2) The lack of lime in most of the streams facilitates the process of retting, whereby the fibres of the flax are separated.

(3) The dampness of the atmosphere facilitates the processes of spinning and weaving.

(4) The early Irish linen industry was greatly improved by the settlement of Protestant refugees who were driven from France at the end of the seventeenth century.

Linen manufacture in Ireland remained in the 'domestic' stage longer than the textile industries of Great Britain, and many hand-loom weavers were at work at the beginning of the present century. With the introduction of power-driven machinery about the middle of last century, however, the industry naturally began to concentrate in Belfast, which had the decisive advantage of cheap imported coal, and that city now dominates the industry to a much greater extent than Manchester and Bradford dominate the textile industries of England. Other centres of the industry are Lurgan, Lisburn, and Larne. Londonderry is engaged in the making of shirts and collars, which together account for half the total value of clothing produced in Northern Ireland. Nearly half the total output of linen goods produced in Northern Ireland is exported, the chief customer being the United States.

Shipbuilding. Belfast ranks next to the Clyde, the Tyne, and the Wear in respect of the tonnage of ships launched. The rise of the shipbuilding industry there is due to the ease of importation of coal and iron, and to the business ability of the masters and the skill of the workmen.

Engineering is carried on chiefly in Belfast, where it arose originally to supply the needs of the shipbuilding and linen industries. The inventive genius of Irish engineers has, however, caused the industry to develop beyond the needs of the locality, so that although marine engineering and the manufacture of linen machinery are predominant, Belfast is noted for a wide range of products, among which may be mentioned machinery for the preparation of tea, electrical machinery, and pumping installations. Other industries, which are also centred in Belfast, are brewing and distilling, the manufacture of ropes, and tobacco.

THE TOWNS OF NORTHERN IRELAND

Belfast with a population of nearly half a million is the capital of Northern Ireland, its largest industrial centre and its busiest port. It owes its pre-eminence largely to its advantageous position. The Lagan valley is like a funnel drawing to the head of Belfast Lough all the trade of the fertile Lough Neagh lowlands, and Belfast is therefore the natural focus of the roads, canals, and railways. This concentration of routes has, indeed, enabled Belfast to draw to itself practically the whole of the overseas trade of the country as well as some of the trade of the Irish Republic. Like Glasgow, however, Belfast owes much to the skill and determination of engineers. One hundred and fifty years ago the present harbour was merely a muddy creek with a depth of only one and a half feet at low water for three miles below the city, but in 1840 the river mouth was dredged, and a new channel cut to enable large liners to reach the heart of the city.

The chief imports are flour, grain, tobacco, coal, clothing, and metals, and the chief exports are dairy produce, bacon, cattle, poultry, linen goods, and ships.

Londonderry, situated twenty-five miles from the sea at the head of Lough Foyle, is the second port of Northern Ireland. The volume of its trade is small, since it serves only the small hinterland of the Foyle valley. Its chief exports are bacon, ham, eggs, and cotton and linen clothing, while its imports consist chiefly of foodstuffs and clothing. *Coleraine*, at the mouth of the Bann, is a small port which has cross-channel services to Liverpool and Glasgow. *Portrush*, near by, is a summer holiday resort, and is the centre from which visitors reach Giant's Causeway.

Larne, situated twenty-five miles north of Belfast, is a minor manufacturing town, and has communication by mail steamer with Stranraer, in southern Scotland. *Newry*, situated at the head of Carlingford Lough, seems fitted by nature to be a rival of Belfast, since it is on a deep and sheltered estuary and controls an easy route to the Lough Neagh lowlands. It has suffered, however, from the competition of Belfast, from the shallowness of its estuary, and from the fact that it lost a large part of its hinterland by the establishment of the Irish Republic. It is, therefore, only of minor importance as a port, though it has some manufacturing industries.

Antrim, the capital of the county of that name, is typical of the small market towns which are dotted over the lowlands. Its population is only two thousand.

THE IRISH REPUBLIC

In order to understand the causes which led to the separation of the Irish Republic from the United Kingdom it is necessary to consider, in broad outline at least, the history of the country from the earliest times. Such a survey cannot be attempted here, but the following points should be borne in mind:

(1) Ireland was never subject to Roman rule, and so her development, though slow, was not broken as in Britain by the withdrawal of the Roman power.

(2) As the Irish had not depended on the Romans for protection, they did not succumb to attacks by the Anglo-Saxons, and so, in spite of later settlements by the Norsemen, the bulk of the people are of the Mediterranean type, like the Welsh and the Gaels.

(3) The Irish were converted to Christianity during the fifth century, and made great advances in civilization while England was in the Dark Ages which followed the Anglo-Saxon invasions.

(4) The obstacles to communication presented by bogs, marshes, and mountains prevented the development of a united government in Ireland, and facilitated the piecemeal conquest of the country first by the Normans and then by Cromwell, but the harsh measures adopted by the Protector did much to embitter the Irish against the English.

(5) Large grants of land were made to English noblemen, many of whom drained off the wealth of the country in rents which were not spent in the country. Thus Ireland became poorer, and the Irish peasantry learnt to regard the English as the source of all their troubles.

(6) The First World War, and the avowed object of Britain and her allies to set free subject peoples, gave great impetus

to the Irish demand for Home Rule, which was granted in 1921 after a bitter struggle.

The Irish Republic is predominantly an agricultural country, two-thirds of the people being directly dependent on the soil for their livelihood. The great majority of the farmers own their farms, only about one-fortieth of the farm land being rented from landlords. The farms are, however, very small, two-thirds of them being less than thirty acres in extent. As the land is not very productive, and the amount of arable land is small (only about 10 per cent of the total surface), the farmers are generally very poor. Much has, however, been done in recent years by the establishment of co-operative creameries, poultry societies, etc., to make it easier for the farmer to dispose of his products, and the Shannon hydro-electric scheme (see page 209) has helped to raise the standard of production.

THE NATURAL DIVISIONS OF THE IRISH REPUBLIC

(1) *The North-west*

This barren, mountainous region is a continuation of the Highlands of Scotland. The coast is of the fiord type, but is fringed in most places by a narrow coastal plain which, together with the sheltered inland valleys, forms the chief area of settlement. The mode of life of the people is very similar to that of the crofters of the Hebrides. Hay, oats, and potatoes are grown on the small farms, and the men go fishing to eke out a scanty subsistence, while the women earn a little money by making the well-known 'Donegal' tweeds. In spite of the unproductivity of the soil the people are passionately fond of their little farms, and the population, though scanty, is too great for the land to support. At Ballyshannon, on Donegal Bay, the river Erne has been harnessed for the generation of hydro-electricity.

The district of Connemara, with its fringing loughs— Mask and Corrib—is noted for its beautiful scenery, and the money spent by tourists does much to relieve the poverty of the people. There are also some quarries in the district which produce marble famed for its green and red colouring.

Sligo, situated at the head of the bay of the same name, is the chief port of the north-west. It is accessible by fairly large ocean-going steamers, and has good rail connections with all parts of the republic, but its total trade is very small, on account of the poverty of its hinterland.

Galway, situated on a sheltered bay, where the Midland Plain reaches the west coast, and immediately opposite Dublin, seems to have a fine position as a port. Some centuries ago it was one of the chief centres for the importation of wine from Spain, but in modern times the decrease in the population of the country, the increase in the size of ships (a belt of hard rock restricts the use of the harbour to vessels drawing not more than sixteen feet of water), and the competition of other ports, have caused its trade to sink into insignificance.

(2) *South-western Ireland*

This region is formed of fold mountains which run roughly from west to east, and which are remnants of a great range which once extended through South Wales, Cornwall, and Brittany to central Europe. The upfolds, which form the ridges, are composed of hard Old Red Sandstone, while the intervening downfolds are formed of carboniferous limestone. At the western edge of the region the ranges have been partially drowned, forming the rias known as Dingle Bay,

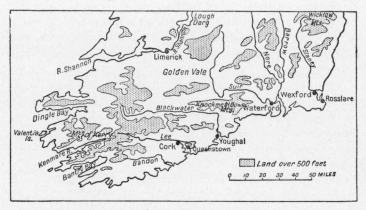

FIG. 76. SOUTHERN IRELAND

Kenmare 'River,' and Bantry Bay. In the east, however, the downfolds are occupied with the longitudinal valleys of the Rivers Bandon, Lee, Blackwater, and Suir. Each of these rivers, however, turns southward near its mouth and enters the sea by a drowned estuary. The River Lee is now being dammed near Cork to provide power for two hydro-electric stations which will supply sixty million units a year.

The mountainous region of Kerry is a thinly peopled pastoral area, the fertile lowlands being given up to cattle and the wind-swept moorlands to sheep. Killarney, with its beautiful lakes, well-wooded glens, and majestic mountains, is the most picturesque district in Ireland.

The river valleys in the eastern two-thirds of the region are among the most fertile and best cultivated parts of the country. As in the rest of Ireland the chief speciality is dairying, and the ease of communication has greatly assisted the growth of co-operative manufacture and marketing of the dairy produce.

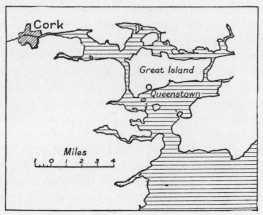

FIG. 77. THE POSITION OF CORK

Cork, the chief city of the region, and the second city and port of the republic, is situated on a fine landlocked harbour formed by the partial drowning of three ridges (see Fig. 77). It exports cattle, pigs, and dairy produce, and imports coal, maize, and wheat. *Cobh* [1] (formerly Queenstown) is a port of call for ocean liners.

(3) *South-eastern Ireland*

(*a*) The Wicklow Mountains are thinly peopled moorlands which rise well over the 2,000-foot line, and in one point attain a height of over 3,000 feet. Sheep are reared on the

[1] Pronounced 'cove.'

mountains, and some agriculture is carried on in the deep, well-wooded valleys.

(b) The south-eastern lowlands, which comprise the counties of Wexford and Carlow, have the advantages of fertile soil, mild winters, warm summers, and comparatively low rainfall. About one-third of the surface is under plough, and large numbers of cattle and pigs are reared.

Waterford, situated at the head of the combined estuary of the Barrow and Suir, is the natural focus of the routes of the south-east. As a port it is concerned chiefly with the importation of foodstuffs and manufactured products, most of its export trade having been taken by Rosslare, the packet station from which there are regular services of mail and passenger steamers to Fishguard in South Wales.

Wexford, situated at the mouth of the Slaney, is another old-established port which has suffered through the competition of Rosslare. It has, however, retained a considerable trade in live cattle, and has a regular service of cattle-boats to Liverpool.

(4) *The Midland Plain*

From the physical and economic standpoint this area may be divided into four sub-regions, viz.:

(a) The coastal plain around Dublin. Here the land is better drained, and the climate is drier and sunnier than in the western districts; consequently there is a greater proportion of arable land, and some wheat and barley are grown, though dairying and stock-raising are the chief specialities.

(b) The central portion. Here the land is waterlogged, communications are difficult, and arable farming is almost impossible. It is therefore devoted chiefly to the raising of cattle, poultry, and pigs. Dairying is not important on account of the difficulty of communication in the waterlogged plain. Much peat is hand-won for domestic fuel, and large excavating machines prepare peat-moss litter for export. There is also a turf-burning electricity plant near the Bog of Allen.

(c) The southern portion, on the fringe of the south-western and the south-eastern mountains. This region includes the

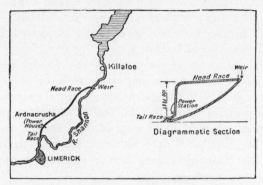

FIG. 78. THE SHANNON HYDRO-ELECTRIC SCHEME

famous Golden Vein which lies to the south of Limerick, and which is the most productive dairying region of the country.

(d) The western portion, beyond the Shannon. The higher parts consist of barren limestone, and the lower parts of peat bogs, only the intermediate slopes being available as farm land. The region is, on the whole, one of the poorest in Ireland.

The *Shannon* is the longest river of the British Isles. It rises within fifty miles of Donegal Bay and winds slowly southward across the plain, widening out at intervals into lakes of which the largest are Loughs Allen, Ree, and Derg. From Lough Allen to Lough Derg the fall averages only six inches per mile, but between Lough Derg and Limerick there is a drop of seven feet per mile. This is sufficient only to create rapids in the stream, but in the Shannon hydro-electric scheme the water is diverted into a canal, or head-race, at Killaloe at the head of the rapids, conducted to Ardnacrusha near the foot of the rapids, and there made to drop a hundred feet on to the turbines which generate the electricity. Though the Shannon and Lough Erne schemes provide the major part of the electricity needed by the Republic, further supplies have to be generated by coal imported at Cork and Dublin.

Limerick, situated at the head of the Shannon estuary, and linked by canal to Dublin, seems to have great advantages as a port. It suffers, however, from its remoteness from the ports of Great Britain, and is, therefore, of minor importance as a port, its imports of coal, timber, and food-stuffs being distributed only within a radius of about thirty miles. The Shannon airport is the starting point of the transatlantic air service.

The ports of the east coast are Dundalk, Drogheda, and Dublin, each situated on a river mouth. *Dundalk* has only a small hinterland, and entry to the harbour is restricted by a bar to vessels drawing less than fifteen feet of water. *Drogheda* can be reached by larger vessels, but has poor railway connections and suffers from its proximity to both Dundalk and Dublin.

Dublin, situated at the mouth of the Liffey, was founded by the Norsemen, who in the ninth century built a fortress on a low hill at the head of navigation of the estuary. It is the chief gateway to the central plain, and in modern times has been made the centre of the systems of canals, roads, and railways of the country. As a port it owes much to the improvements made by engineers, the depth of the channel having been increased from six feet, as it was in its natural state, to thirty-two feet.

The exports consist chiefly of cattle, sheep, and pigs, which are sent to Holyhead and Birkenhead, and there slaughtered.

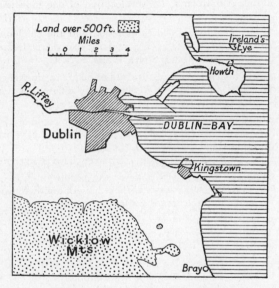

FIG. 79. THE POSITION OF DUBLIN

Other important items of export are whisky, dairy produce, and hides.

As a manufacturing centre Dublin is far behind Belfast, but it has some shipyards, engineering shops, and linen factories, and many breweries and distilleries.

Kingstown, or Dun Laoghaire (pronounced 'Leery'), is the outport for Dublin, and is the terminus of the passenger service from Holyhead.

EXAMINATION QUESTIONS

1. Why is it that the principal occupation of the people of Ireland is that of farming? State and account for (*a*) the characteristic type of farming in Ireland; (*b*) the location of one industrial area. (N. U.)

2. Describe the broad features of relief, and the chief industrial activities in *one* of the following regions: Northern Ireland, the central Lowlands of Scotland, South Wales. (N. U.)

3. Which of the two countries, Ireland or Scotland, do you consider can be more easily divided into a few clearly differentiated natural regions? Give reasons for your answer. (L. G. S.)

4. The north-east corner of Ireland has much in common, from the point of view of both physical and political geography, with the south-west of Scotland. How? (L. G. S.)

5. Describe the climate and relief of (*a*) Shannon basin; (*b*) Clyde basin. State the chief occupations of the people in each of these areas, and show to what extent they have been determined or rendered possible by the climate and relief. (L. M.)

6. Describe and account for the principal agricultural and industrial activities of Northern Ireland, and draw a sketch-map to show where they occur. (D. S. C.)

7. Describe the physical geography and the agriculture of the central plains of Ireland and show the importance of the port of Dublin in relation to this region. (D. M.)

8. Shipbuilding has for long been an important industry of the British Isles. Name *three* of the most important centres and show what advantages they have for this industry. (D. S. C.)

9. Show, by sketch-maps, the sites of Limerick, Newcastle, Gloucester, and Liverpool, and explain how the site has influenced the growth of the port in each case. (L. M.)

10. Compare and contrast the occupations of the people in, and the geographical conditions of, the central plain of Ireland with those of the Weald. (L. M.)

11. Contrast eastern England with the Shannon basin with respect to climate, and the resulting types of farming. (L. G. S.)

12. The four capital cities of the British Isles, London, Edinburgh, Dublin, and Belfast, all face east. Discuss the advantages each derives from such a situation. (L. G. S.)

13. What geographical causes account for the great difference in density of population between the Lowlands of Scotland and the central plains of Ireland? (C. S. C.)

14. What factors affect the distribution of population in Ireland? Account for the absence of large towns on the western coasts.

(D. S. C.)

15. Essex and County Kerry are roughly in the same latitude. Describe and account for the differences in the climatic conditions of these counties. (O. S. C.)

16. Write an account of the relief and drainage of Ulster, and show how these facts have affected the position of ports and the means of communication within the country. (O. S. C.)

17. What geographical facts account for the smaller proportion of arable land in Ireland than in Scotland? (O. S. C.)

18. Describe the climate of Northern Ireland, and give an account of the chief occupations of the people of that region. (C. S. C.)

19. 'Ireland is economically a poor country.' What geographical conditions support this statement? (O. S. C.)

20. Describe, in general terms, the characteristic features, and explain the chief occupations, in two of the following areas, *one* from each pair: (*a*) north-west Ireland *or* south-east Ireland; (*b*) the Southern Uplands of Scotland *or* the Highlands (north of Caledonian Canal). (C. S. C.)

21. The largest towns in Scotland are situated on the midland plain (the central Lowlands); the largest towns in Ireland are on or near the coast. Account for this distribution of towns.

Choose *one* large Scottish town and *one* large Irish town, and with regard to each explain why it has become a centre of population.

(C. S. C.)

CHAPTER XVII

ECONOMIC SURVEY

Iron and Steel

The principal features of the iron and steel industries of Britain are shown on the map opposite (Fig. 80).

Iron ore. The Jurassic escarpment which runs through the counties of Oxfordshire, Northamptonshire, Leicestershire, and Lincolnshire supplies over 90 per cent of our home-produced iron ore; about 3 per cent of our total supplies are provided by the northern extension of this escarpment in the Cleveland Hills; and a small quantity of high-grade hematite ore is mined in the Furness district. Imports of iron ore are roughly equal to the home production, the chief sources of supply being Canada, Sweden, North Africa, Spain, and Sierra Leone.

Pig-iron is produced mainly in the ore-mining districts and on coastal coal-fields where coke and imported ore meet. The north-west coast and the iron-mining districts of the Jurassic escarpment (except in the Frodingham district of north Lincolnshire) produce a surplus of pig-iron for sale elsewhere in Britain, while the steel works of Sheffield, and to a very large extent those of the Black Country, depend on pig-iron brought in from other districts.

Shipbuilding is concentrated chiefly on the Clyde estuary, which produces about a third of our total output; the estuaries of the Tyne, Wear, and Tees, which supply 40 per cent of the total; and Belfast, Barrow, and Birkenhead, which together produce about 18 per cent.

Engineering employs more people than any other single industry in Britain. The 'heavy' engineering industry is concentrated chiefly in those districts which provide a market

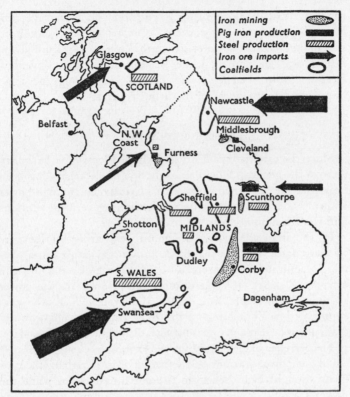

FIG. 80. IRON AND STEEL

for the product; e.g. textile machinery in Lancashire and
Yorkshire, locomotives at various depots on the main railway
lines, and farm machinery in the agricultural market towns.

The *motor-car* and *aeroplane* industries draw their raw
materials and component parts from such varied sources that
they have developed not so much in the older industrial districts as in newer areas which have good communications by

road and rail, wide areas for expansion and attractive residential districts for the workers. Centres specially noted for the manufacture of motor-cars are Coventry, Birmingham, Luton, and Dagenham, while Bristol, Gloucester, Coventry, Derby, Luton, Hatfield, and Hayes are among the most important aeroplane manufacturing centres.

ELECTRICITY SUPPLIES

Since the establishment of the British Electricity Authority in 1926 the generation and transmission of electricity has been organized on a national basis, with a Grid system of high-power transmission lines to link up the various generating stations and the consuming areas.

In the industrial areas the main generating stations are situated on or near the coal-fields and on navigable waterways which facilitate the transport of coal and the disposal of waste ash (see Fig. 81). Of outstanding importance are the power stations on the rivers Aire, Calder, and Trent, which draw coal supplies from Yorkshire and the East Midlands, and 'export' a surplus of electricity to southern England and Lancashire.

The supplies of electricity for the London area are generated chiefly at power stations on the banks of the Thames, the coal being brought in by sea from the north-east coast, while the power stations in the south-west draw their coal from South Wales.

Atomic Power. It is estimated that by 1975 atomic energy will supply about 20 per cent of the country's total needs of power. The chief atomic power stations at present in operation or in course of construction are situated at Calder Hall in Cumberland, Chapelcross in Dumfriesshire, Bradwell in Essex, Berkeley in Gloucestershire, and Hinkley Point near Bridgewater.

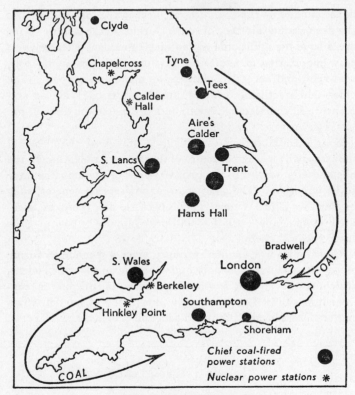

FIG. 81. ELECTRICAL POWER

THE CHEMICAL INDUSTRY

The most important branches of the 'heavy' chemical industry are those which are based on salt, coal, and petroleum respectively.

The Middle Mersey and Tees-side are the chief areas where extensive chemical industries are based primarily on nearby deposits of salt—the Cheshire salt-field in the former case and the deep-seated salt-beds of south Durham in the latter. Both areas have the additional advantages of navigable waterways, easy importation of additional raw materials, proximity to a coal-field, and access to markets at home and abroad. The chief manufacturing centres are Northwich, Widnes, and Runcorn in the Mersey region, and Billingham-on-Tees in the latter (see pages 72 and 81).

Soap manufacture is essentially a branch of the chemical industry, which supplies many of its raw materials, though the oils and fats which are the primary basis of the industry have to be imported. The chief soap manufacturing centres, such as Port Sunlight, Widnes, and Newcastle are, therefore, situated on navigable estuaries, and near supplies of coal and the basic 'heavy' chemicals.

Glass is also a 'chemical' product, since it is made by fusing silica with sodium carbonate and other chemicals. St Helens, which is the chief glass-making centre in Britain, is conveniently situated for the ready assembling of imported raw materials and locally produced coal and chemicals.

CHEMICALS FROM COAL

When coal is heated in coke ovens and enclosed retorts the volatile matter is driven off and coke and other forms of smokeless fuel remain. From the volatile substances, and from the residue of coal tar, innumerable chemical products such as ammonia, benzine, and creosote are obtained and these in turn are the basis for the manufacture of drugs, dyes, plastics, paint, synthetic rubber, antiseptics, fertilizers, nylon, and a host of other substances. The chemical industries based on coal are, naturally, situated on or near the coal-fields.

FIG. 82. OIL-REFINING AND PETROCHEMICAL CENTRES

PETROCHEMICALS

Petroleum is a mixture of various substances which are separated by refining to give petrol, paraffin, fuel oil, lubricating oil, etc. Moreover, by the chemical processes known as 'cracking' the molecules in the crude petroleum may be 'cracked' and recombined to make completely new compounds, which in their turn are used as the basis for the manufacture of most of the substances which can be made from coal, besides some unique materials such as terylene.

The chief oil-refining and petrochemical centres of Britain are shown in Fig. 82.

MINOR INDUSTRIES

Leather. In former times tanning was carried on in almost every locality, but the industry is now concentrated in (a) certain inland towns where the demands of local industries have favoured the development of old-established tanneries, e.g. Northampton and Leicester, which specialize in the making of the lighter leathers for the 'uppers' of shoes, and (b) the major ports—London, Liverpool, Glasgow, Newcastle, Bristol, etc.—where the specialization is in the manufacture of the heavier types of leather from our great imports of hides and skins.

Paper. The chief factors which have determined the location of the paper-making industry are: proximity to the imports of the wood pulp which is the raw material for all but the very highest grades of paper, easy distribution of the bulky product to nearby 'markets,' and an abundant supply of pure water for the manufacturing processes. The chief manufacturing areas are: the Medway valley and estuary in Kent, Merseyside and mid Lancashire, and Midlothian and Fifeshire.

Paint. The chief raw materials used in the manufacture of paint are vegetable oils, which are made from imported linseed and other vegetable products, and pigments and synthetic resins which are products of the chemical industries. The industry is therefore carried on mainly near the great ports—London, Hull, Bristol, etc.—or in association with the chemical industry as on Merseyside.

EXAMINATION QUESTIONS FOR GENERAL REVISION

1. Give a reasoned account of the type of farming in *three* of the following: Kent, Cheshire, Hereford, Fife, Kerry.   (L. M.)

2. Explain what you mean by the following terms: a faulted valley, river capture, rain-shadow.   Describe them with the aid of sketches and say how they were caused.   Name one example of each in the British Isles.   (D. M.)

3. What parts of the British Isles are notable for the production of (a) butter and eggs; (b) wool; (c) sugar-beet?   Give reasons for the distribution you mention.   (L. G. S.)

4. On the outline map of the British Isles provided:
(a) Insert and number one line of latitude and one of longitude;
(b) Draw an approximate scale of miles (stating how obtained or calculated);
(c) Mark and name four coal-fields (including one in Wales and one in Scotland);
(d) Mark by dots and name the following ten towns: Belfast, Dublin, Inverness, Dundee, Carlisle, Birmingham, Aberystwyth, Plymouth, Norwich, and Hull.
(e) Shade the areas producing important quantities of *wheat* and *flax*.   (L. G. S.)

5. Write an explanatory account of the industries carried on at *four* of the following towns, with special reference to the sources of the raw materials used: Burton, Birmingham, Bristol, Northampton, Stoke, Swansea.   (L. G. S.)

6. Name *one* town in districts noted for each of the following manufactures in the British Isles: pottery, linen, cutlery, boots, cycles, chocolate.   Give reasons for the location of the industries named.   (D. S. C.)

7. Give an account of the distribution of population in England (excluding Wales), noting especially the geographical factors which have influenced that distribution.   (L. G. S.)

8. Name *one* district in England important for iron-smelting, and *one* for coal-exporting. Show how position and geographical conditions favour each activity.   (C. S. C.)

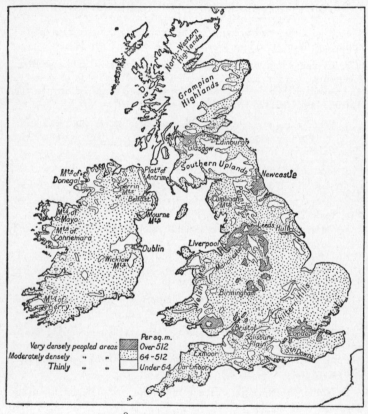

FIG. 83. DENSITY OF POPULATION

9. Select *one* of the following regions of the British Isles: Southern Uplands of Scotland, south-western Ireland (west of Waterford), south-eastern England (Kent, Surrey, and Sussex). Illustrating your answer by a map, describe the region under the following

headings: (a) chief features of relief; (b) *either* chief routes in relation to the relief *or* characteristic farming activities.   (N. U.)

10. Illustrating your answers by sketch-maps, show the geographical factors which have contributed to the growth of (a) York *or* Crewe as a railway centre; (b) Hull *or* Leith as a port; (c) Lincoln *or* Norwich as an agricultural market town.   (N. U.)

11. Select *two* of the following: heavy chemicals, pottery, extraction of metals from their ores, wool textile industry, market gardening.   (a) Name *one* area in England or Wales associated with *each* of the industries selected; (b) draw a sketch-map of each of the two areas; (c) state the geographical conditions which affect the industries in these particular areas.   (N. U.)

12. Select *one* of the following regions of the British Isles; central plain of Ireland, south-west peninsula of England, the Hampshire basin, East Anglia.   Illustrating your answer by a map, describe the region under the following headings: (a) chief features of relief (including river systems); (b) chief farming activities in relation to soil and climate; (c) the part played in the economic life of the region by *two* towns shown on your map.   (N. U.)

13. Describe (a) the relief and drainage; (b) the chief routes in relation to the relief, in *one* of the following areas: the Pennines; the Southern Uplands of Scotland; the Weald.   (N. U.)

14. Select two British coal-fields which have very different industries other than coal-mining.   In the case of each coal-field (a) give its position; (b) mention its chief towns; and (c) account briefly for the development of its chief industry.   (N. U.)

15. Flax is imported into Ireland, jute into Scotland, and cotton into England.   In the case of each country, (a) state for what industry the import is required; (b) name one area where the industry is carried on; and (c) account briefly for the location of the industry in the area named.   (N. U.)

16. Choose *one* town from each of the following pairs, and, in each case, (a) describe its position, and (b) indicate the geographical conditions which have contributed to its importance: (i) Carlisle, Crewe; (ii) Dublin, Bristol; (iii) Edinburgh, York.   (N. U.)

17. Draw a large sketch-map of *one* of the following coal-mining areas, showing the positions of its principal towns: (a) Lanark (Clyde); (b) Northumberland and Durham; (c) Yorks, Derby, and Notts.

Name one important manufacturing industry of the area chosen, and state the factors which have contributed to its development.

(N. U.)

18. Illustrate *two* of the following statements by means of sketch-maps: (*a*) the more important Irish ports are conveniently situated for trade with Great Britain; (*b*) Perth and Stirling grew up as gap towns situated at bridge-heads: (*c*) the main railway lines leave the London basin by gaps in the chalk hills.   (N. U.)

19. Name *one* important industry located at Hull, *one* at Liverpool, and *one* at Bristol.   In the case of each industry, account for its location at the port concerned and give the chief sources of its raw materials.   (N. U.)

20. State the principal occupations of the people of two of the following areas, and show how these occupations are related to the natural resources: (*a*) the Southern Uplands of Scotland; (*b*) the county of Glamorgan; (*c*) south-eastern Ireland.   (C. S. L.)

21. Describe the geographical conditions which have aided *two* of the following: (*a*) the building of ships on the banks of the Tyne; (*b*) the manufacture of linen goods in Northern Ireland; (*c*) the manufacture of woollen goods in the Tweed valley.

22. Where are the chief iron-smelting districts of Great Britain? For *one* of these districts discuss the principal factors which have led to the location of the industry there.   (N. U.)

23. Describe carefully the position of the following ports: Bristol, Hull, Dover, and Pembroke Dock.   Compare the natural advantages possessed by them.   (O. S. C.)

24. Describe the scenery and surface features of *two* of the following: the Pennine Chain of England; the central plain of Ireland; the South Downs; the Southern Uplands of Scotland.   (C. S. C.)

25. How has the commercial development of the British Isles been influenced by their (*a*) position; (*b*) climate; (*c*) mineral wealth?

(C. S. C.)

26. What regions are included under 'Industrial England'? Describe the geographical position of the chief industrial centres, mentioning the industries which belong to each.   (C. S. C.)

27. Name *three* ports in Great Britain which are largely concerned with the export of coal.   Describe their position and their relation to

the coal-fields which they serve.   What other industries have centred round each coal-field ?   (C. S. C.)

28. At least four regions in England and one each in Wales, Scotland, and Ireland show a very dense population to the square mile.   Locate these regions and examine *briefly* the causes of their crowded population.   (L. G. S.)

29. What do you understand by the Hampshire basin, the Welsh borders, the Scottish Highlands, Connemara?
Choose *one* of the four and discuss its geographical conditions and their effects on human activities.   (L. G. S.)

30. Give a concise and coherent account of the geographical conditions *either* of the plain of York, *or* central Ireland, *or* of some small region in Britain which you have specially studied.   (L. G. S.)

31. Describe briefly the course of *one* of these three rivers: Trent, Shannon, Clyde.   Indicate the towns and industries it serves, and how it serves them.   (L. M.)

32. Discuss the location and importance of navigable waterways in the central plain of England, *or* in that of Scotland, *or* in that of Ireland.   (L. G. S.)

33. Taking at least three localities as examples, discuss the geographical conditions under which the shipbuilding industry has developed in the British Isles.   (L. M.)

34. Explain clearly the conditions which are most suitable for sheep.   Draw a sketch-map of England and Wales, shading and naming (*a*) the principal sheep-rearing areas; and (*b*) three wool-manufacturing districts.   (D. M.)

35. Select three areas in the British Isles important respectively for *each* of the following, and mention the geographical features favouring the occupation mentioned in *one* area in each case: (*a*) rearing of beef cattle; (*b*) shipbuilding; (*c*) manufacture of boots and shoes.   (L. G. S.)

36. What do you understand by a hinterland?   Show your meaning exactly by reference to *three* of the following ports: Dublin, Glasgow, Southampton, Cardiff.   (L. G. S.)

37. Give an account of the geographical features and characteristic occupations in *two* of the following areas: the Tweed basin; the hinterland of Cardiff; the hinterland of Cork.   (L. G. S.)

38. Describe the position and the characteristic features of *two* of the following: (*a*) the Chilterns; (*b*) the north York moors; (*c*) the Pentland Hills; (*d*) the plateau of Antrim.

Show how each has affected its immediate surroundings.   (C. S. C.)

39. Choose *two* of the following pairs of towns for discussion: (*a*) Aberdeen and Inverness; (*b*) Cork and Limerick; (*c*) Birmingham and Gloucester.   Contrast the towns in each selected pair from the point of view of position and advantages for development.

(L. M.)

40. According to the census of 1951, there were in Scotland 5,000,000 people, in Wales 2,600,000 people, and in England 41,100,000 people.   With the aid of a sketch-map or maps, give a brief account of the geographical factors which have affected such a distribution of population.

41. Describe a railway journey from St. Pancras to Carlisle. What effect has the relief of the country passed through had on the direction taken by this line of rail?   (L. M.)

42. Name the characteristic type of farming in *three* of the following districts: Romney Marsh, the Fens, Oxford Clay Vale, East Anglia, Northern Ireland.   What advantages does each of the selected areas possess for carrying on this particular type of farming?

(L. M.)

43. Analyse the geographical positions of Newcastle, Fishguard, Blackpool, and Bolton, and show how geographical conditions affect the main occupations of the people in each.   (L. M.)

44. What is meant by market gardening?   How far is its development in England influenced in the growth of large towns?   Compare the density of population in a market-gardening area with that in a dairy-farming area, and give reasons for any differences.

(O. S. C.)

45. Describe *either* the Southern Uplands of Scotland *or* the Southern Highlands of Ireland under the headings of (*a*) general relief of the land; (*b*) effect of the relief upon local industries.   (L. M.)

46. Navigable waterways are of much importance in accounting for the conversion of insignificant towns into great commercial centres.   Examine this statement with special reference to any *one*

striking example in the British Isles, describing and showing the importance of the waterway or waterways concerned.   (L. M.)

47. How far may we attribute the rise and progress of each of the towns, Birmingham, Hull, Paisley, and Londonderry, to geographical position and natural resources?   (L. M.)

48. Select *one* only of the following rivers: Trent, Tweed, Boyne. Indicate the chief physical features and natural resources of its basin, and point out the resultant human activities.   (L. M.)

49. Write a descriptive geographical account of any *two* of the following areas and their inhabitants: the Pennines, the Outer Hebrides, County Donegal.   (L. M.)

50. Examine the distribution of population in *either* Wales *or* the southern half of Scotland.   Point out any striking features and account for them.   (L. M.)

51. On the given map of the British Isles mark clearly and name the following: (*a*) the chalk uplands; (*b*) the courses of the Trent and the Tweed; (*c*) the most important sheep-rearing areas; (*d*) land in Wales that lies above 2,000 ft. (approximately).   (W. M.)

52. What are the chief ports of Great Britain for the import of (*a*) fruit; (*b*) timber?   From what countries do these products largely come?   (D. S. C.)

53. Describe the position and occupation of *two* of the following towns: Dundee, Edinburgh, Bristol, Nottingham.   (D. M.)

54. Give an account of the geographical factors underlying three of the following: the motor-car industry in the English Midlands; agricultural machinery at Bedford or Lincoln; aluminium production in the west Highlands of Scotland; glass, soap, and chemicals in south-west Lancashire; tin plates in South Wales.   (D. M.)

55. What do you understand by three of the phrases: (*a*) the mean April temperature of Durham is 44·1°; (*b*) the west of Scotland affords many typical examples of fiords; (*c*) boulder-clay and other glacial deposits cover much of south Durham (county); (*d*) a depression is situated off the Hebrides?   (D. M.)

56. 'In some areas iron is mined; in others it is smelted; elsewhere it is used for manufacturing purposes.'   Apply this statement to the British Isles, and explain the distribution of the industries.   (O. S. C.)

57. Discuss the geographical factors which affect the distribution of population shown by the following statistics:

County	Area in Acres	Population
Devon . .	1,671,364	709,614
Glamorgan .	520,456	1,120,910
Argyll . .	1,990,472	76,862

(C. S. C.)

58. Explain in detail what is meant by any *two* of the following: the fiord coast of Scotland, the Fens, the continental shelf of Europe, the scarplands of England.   (O. S. C.)

59. Account fully for *two only* of the following: (a) the Highlands are the most sparsely peopled part of Scotland; (b) Lancashire has now a denser population than Suffolk, though that was not always so; (c) Glamorgan is the most densely peopled county in Wales; (d) the population of Ireland is fairly evenly distributed throughout the country.   (O. S. C.)

60. Describe and account for the characteristics of the surface features of *two* of the following: (a) the central plain of Ireland; (b) the Grampians; (c) Dartmoor; (d) the English Midlands.   (O. S. C.)

61. Of what advantages to its inhabitants are the tides and tidal currents around the shores of Great Britain?   (O. S. C.)

62. State and account for the principal occupations of the inhabitants of *one* of the following: (a) Northern Ireland; (b) North Wales; (c) the coal-fields of the English Midlands.   (O. S. C.)

63. Show how the physical features of the land have influenced the course of the main railways in *one* of the following areas: south-west England, northern England, Wales. Your answer must be illustrated by a sketch-map.   (C. S. C.)

64. Compare the winter conditions of life and occupations of the inhabitants in (a) the Hebrides; (b) the Pennine uplands; (c) the Weald of Kent.   (C. S. C.)

65. Carefully describe the position, and discuss the reasons for the

growth or importance of *four* of the following towns: Middlesbrough, Limerick, Lincoln, Londonderry, Reading, Torquay.   (O. S. C.)

66. Indicate the *three* most important iron ore-mining areas in Great Britain, and give some account of the industries making use of that ore.   (O. S. C.)

67. Select *three* areas from the British Isles, each with a different type of soil.   Describe, and give reasons for, any differences in vegetation, both natural and cultivated, in the three areas.   (O. S. C.)

68. Describe the occupations and account for their distribution in any *one* of the following areas: the Thames basin, Ulster, the West Riding of Yorkshire, South Wales.   (O. S. C.)

69. Write an account of the manufacturing industries in *one* of the following coal-fields: south Yorkshire, north Staffordshire, Lanarkshire, South Wales.   (O. S. C.)

70. What would be the chief changes that would occur in the coastline if the British Isles were (*a*) submerged 600 ft; (*b*) uplifted 600 ft?   (O. S. C.)

71. Select *three* of the following industries and indicate for each *one* area in the British Isles where it is carried on.   State clearly the conditions favouring the development of each of the three, and name the chief centres—chair-making, sugar-refining, linen manufacture, tin-plating, hop production, glass manufacture, slate-quarrying.

(O. S. C.)

72. The Irish Republic and Scotland differ only slightly in area. Account for the contrasts shown by the statistics given in each of the columns.

		Irish Republic	Scotland
Total area	1,000 acres	17,000	19,000
1. Good pasture		8,000	1,500
2. Rough grass and heath		2,000	10,000
3. Wheat		25	50
4. Cattle	thou- sands	4,800	1,100
5. Sheep		4,250	8,000
6. Total population		2,970	4,840

(N. U.)

INDEX